Becoming a Millennial Veterinarian

◆ ◆ ◆

As Told by a Fellow Millennial Vet,
Ashley Gray, DVM @southernpetvet

Ashley Gray

I want to start by thanking all of the role models
in my life. Mentorship is the key
to surviving in this profession, and I am
lucky to have found great mentors over the years.
I especially want to thank Amanda, Kerri,
and my mom Kelly for their support
on my first literary journey.
I could not have done this without your help!

1. WHO IS @SOUTHERNPET-VET?

Looking back on the last twenty years, I remember dreaming of becoming a veterinarian like it was yesterday. Almost every child proclaims at some point "I want to be a veterinarian when I grow up." I hear that all the time from clients, and I most certainly fit into that cliché. Granted, there was a brief stint in time when I thought I could be a singer (I am an off-tune alto by the way), but hey, a girl can dream!

My love for animals was nurtured early on by my parents. I was born and raised in Virginia where I grew up in the suburbs outside of Richmond. My younger sister and I both shared a love for animals, and for some reason, my parents didn't feel we needed to be cut off on the number of pets we had. Due to this, my husband learned early on in our relationship that he had to cap the number of pets we have, or I would quickly take advantage. In case you were wondering, I am allowed three pets, but then I casually snuck in a fourth dog so I am definitely cut off now. We currently have four adopted animals (two Australian Shepherd mixes and two long haired cats). Growing up, my parents were always open to any pet my little heart desired and helped teach me how to care for each one. I remember one day we were at the pet store, and my family and I decided to take home a pair of finches. A few months later, I was witnessing reproduction at its finest as I watched eggs hatch into babies. It was so cool! This theme continued to guinea pigs where my dad found out the hard way that the pet store sold me a pregnant guinea pig... I came running downstairs one day screaming, "There are a bunch of guinea pig babies!!!!" You can imagine the look on my dad's face as I led him upstairs.... You name it, and I tried to raise it.

When my sister and I got older, our parents decided it was time to take our mini petting zoo and move to the country. We moved about an hour away outside of Charlottesville to a 218-acre farm with a river that ran through it. As you can probably extrapolate, our zoo expanded to large animals. We had miniature donkeys and even a dwarf Angus cow that we saved from slaughter who used to love to mount all the other small ruminants at the most awkward times! I spent my time before and after school bottle-feeding Angus calves and goat kids, riding Quarter horses, and playing with our many barn cats in the hayloft. Over time, being around all these different animals instilled me with a strong passion that drove me to dedicate my life toward becoming a veterinarian.

After months of volunteering in various small animal hospitals throughout high school and college, I realized that I could handle the parts of the job that were considered difficult by many of my fellow millennial classmates who opted for other career paths. There are many difficult sides to the job: emergent cases, financial limitations, and the added dimension that pets are beloved family members that make it a difficult career choice. I am glad that a lot of people do not choose this path for those reasons. The veterinary profession is not for everyone, and it can definitely take a toll on you. For me, as time progressed, my love for the veterinary profession kept growing. When talking to most vet students over the years, the funny part is that many of us change our minds often when it comes to the type of medicine we want to practice. I myself went from thinking I could be an equine vet at the racetrack to deciding small animal medicine was better suited to me.

I always had my eyes set on college at Virginia Tech. I started there as an undergraduate with a Food Science degree and Equine Production minor. I knew veterinary school was extremely competitive so I thought a different degree would help in case vet school did not work out. Let's get real when you look at the statistics: Virginia Techs' vet class of 2022 had 1,656 students apply for a total of 126 admissions. That's a 7.6% acceptance rate! I am still in shock that I even got an interview with those odds. If I did not get into vet school, my plan was to find a job in the pet food industry. Thankfully, after two tries, I got accepted in the summer of 2010.

As I mentioned earlier, I originally thought equine medicine was my path. I loved working outside, making house calls, and being surrounded by gorgeous horses. Over time, I realized that the lifestyle might not be for me after I spent some time shadowing an equine veterinarian. I came home exhausted every evening! I can't begin to tell you how much I respect large animal veterinarians after these experiences. I learned that as an equine vet it can be prohibitively expensive to have an assistant, which means the vet may not have trained help when managing the high-strung, less well-mannered horses. It also meant that I, as the extern, was lugging the expensive, heavy x-ray equipment back and forth. That was the summer I also learned to value biceps. The best part of vet school is that you have time to decide what you want to do, and we all find our niche. I found myself constantly being drawn to small animal medicine topics throughout school, and after my first year, small animal medicine was it.

I found the more tedious subjects in vet school were in the first year. I still have nightmares about how many ATP are created in the Kreb's Cycle. I laugh looking back because I have to google the answer now. I understand why these classes are important, but they certainly aren't preparatory for a profession out in the real world. As school progressed, I did feel prepared with my knowledge base, but the areas I felt somewhat lacking in were efficiency, confidence, and organization. I found that I struggled throughout my clinical year to examine a patient and then transition my findings into a logical work-up plan for my differentials. I began to feel like a deer in headlights when my turn came in rounds. You know that feeling when the clinician everyone is afraid of calls you out, and the bile starts to rise in your throat as you get all red and sweaty-palmed. I do not miss those days! Don't get me wrong... clinics are amazing. After studying nonstop for three years, there is nothing better than being able to touch animals again and communicate with their owners. I still remember one of my favorite cases where a puppy swallowed part of a bone, and it tore through his esophagus. I had him as my patient for ten days on my internal medicine rotation. I can look back on it fondly now, but gosh how tedious it was to do all those esophageal tube feedings multiple times a day. I really got to know those owners well, and it further strengthened my opinion that I wanted to be the doctor with regular clients. A doctor who helps care for their furry children like my own.

I do feel that vet school struggles in some areas to prepare you for a real-world career. You must use your outside rotations and added experiences to get the skills necessary to be a professional in a busy hospital. Some of the main reasons why clinics are lacking as compared to the "real world" are efficiency and caseload. I remember having one to two cases maximum on Internal Medicine, and it would take all day to work them up as I bounced between radiology, internal medicine, anesthesia, etc. This is not very efficient and makes it extremely difficult for graduates to transition and see appointments every 20-30 minutes. The other area lacking is caseload. This is no fault of vet school as the majority of cases have already been pre-screened by another doctor and are being sent for an advanced work-up. I still have nightmares about my first ear infection after graduation when I just felt silly trying to remember how to read an ear cytology while remembering the drugs I forgot from Dermatology two years prior. The real truth of it is that the majority of the cases you see in school you may never see again. When I am mentoring, my favorite phrase for interns is to forget about the zebras initially, as vet school pretty much shows you the zebras front and center. It does not mean they are not out there, but we just have to retrain our brain to focus on the big picture before we narrow down our differential diagnoses.

Vet schools have realized this area of deficiency for a while now and are taking active measures to better prepare students for the real world. I am extremely happy to see that most schools nowadays are getting their students into the clinics earlier than their last year. We are also seeing more case-based learning models, which are extremely important to professional growth and are part of why I opted to do an internship. Primary case responsibility will force you to start making decisions and is the only true way to gain confidence in yourself. There comes a point where you just need to jump in and take the leap from student to acting as the doctor. I know I would have remembered things better if they were not just words on a page but rather cases I helped to actively manage.

I chose to pursue an internship after graduation so I could have strong mentorship and organized growth in order to become the clinician I aspired to be. I did not feel strongly about specializing but wanted to keep my options open. I learned so much about myself as a doctor in my first year on an emotional, professional, and physical level. I still remember some days deliriously writing records at 11 pm after a 15-hour workday, but I wouldn't trade it for another experience. I believe that my internship made me a more successful veterinarian earlier in my career. It helped mold me into a high producing, confident doctor with a strong medical and surgical background. I never thought I would be where I am five years out from school and attribute it to being pushed outside of my comfort zone in a structured learning environment. That being said, I do feel you can get there without an internship, but that is part of why you are reading this book.

I graduated from my internship and decided to stay on as an associate at the same hospital. The set up of my work environment has been a large 12+ doctor teaching hospital, open 24/7, in a busy metropolitan area. It has allowed me to practice high quality medicine with all the bells and whistles. I am exposed to every income tax bracket, which has helped me to adapt my style of medicine to a variety of price points. I began my career as an emergency clinician working overnights, and I felt adequately prepared for it after my internship year. For a short while, I enjoyed the whole "7 on 7 off" work mentality. Then, a few months in, I realized how much I missed the general practice atmosphere. I knew that what made me the happiest was the idea of having clients and patients that I see on a routine basis, and I wanted to be their family doctor. I transitioned from night to day walker and have been doing a mix of daytime emergency, appointment days, and general surgery/dentistry ever since then. I have enjoyed working in a large teaching hospital, but it is not for everyone. It is important to start considering what you like early on in your career to find the right fit for you.

I took over the role of internship director a few years ago and was ecstatic for the opportunity. I didn't mention it earlier, but I was social chair and pledge mom of my sorority in college (Go Tridelta!) so this was the perfect fit for me. Since I had been through the internship process recently, I recognized some of the anxieties when first starting out. I found that I really loved teaching and wanted to grow young professional veterinarians. I have watched many new veterinarians ask similar questions and go through comparable experiences. I understand first hand how some days you feel like you diagnose everything correctly while cuddling puppies and kittens, and then other days you feel like you do not know anything at all and literally get pooped on. It really is an uphill battle the first year, but I promise it is worth it once you have a year under your belt.

There are many topics that aren't touched on in depth in school related to our professional development. Not to mention, times are VERY different from when our colleagues graduated 20+ years ago. The digital age has taken over causing new societal demands and stressors that we now face daily. It has made many clients expect accessibility, and if they do not feel we are meeting their demands, they will take their irritated voices to social media through Facebook or online reviews. This puts a lot of pressure on us to be readily available and has started to make many of us feel like we work in a service industry rather than a medical profession. These new demands paired with a high stress career have caused a notable rise in the suicide rate among veterinarians. In the last few years, it has been a hot topic with statistics as high as one in six veterinarians having suicidal thoughts. By preparing for the rigors of our profession early, you will be able to start out on the right foot from the beginning.

So, get excited my fellow veterinary students and new graduates! We are about to dig into some topics that will help you take the leap from student to professional. I have put together my first hand experience with data I have been analyzing over the last few years about our profession. I want you to think of me as your guide on this professional journey. One who aims to get you on solid footing earlier in your career. I cannot express enough the significance of how becoming a Millennial or Generation Z veterinarian is much different than it was for previous generations. By the end of our time together, you will be provided with education and resources that will allow you to tailor your unique experience to your career goals. I want to see each and every one of you transition seamlessly into this rewarding profession.

2. THE MARKET TODAY

There are always going to be changes in the veterinary industry due to multiple factors. Our market will vary based on how the economy is doing, location, or the numbers of positions for hire. I know that my statistics here may change as the book ages, but my hope is to express how the market is at this point in time (2018-2019) to give you a realistic picture of the veterinary landscape. The numbers will always vary to a degree, but there are some striking trends that will most likely continue on in future years.

Debt is a four-letter word most of us quickly ignore as we apply for our student loans. According to the AVMA, the harsh reality is that average student debt of all veterinary graduates in 2016, including those with zero debt, was $143,757.82. The average when you only look at students with debt is higher at $167,534.89. OUCH! Even scarier is that 20% of students have greater than $200,000 in debt weighing on their shoulders at the end of vet school. These are striking numbers and illustrate the scary debt burden that a lot of us face upon graduation. The harsh reality is that our profession has an extremely high debt to income ratio at almost 2:1. This is important to wrap your head around early because it may affect your choice of career path come graduation.

Most of you may not have started your job search yet or have any idea what current income stats are in our profession. Clinics, NAVLE, and internship VIRMP applications pretty much consume the first six months of your senior year of vet school. With debt ever present, it is important to start getting an idea of what you can expect as a starting salary. There are a variety of factors that influence your salary offer from your future employer. Some factors you can control, and others you cannot.

Experience: Typically, as a new graduate, you can expect to have a baseline salary, which can be difficult to negotiate. Some jobs will offer a salary plus a percentage of your production, but it will depend on the hospital. Unfortunately, it is hard to negotiate as a new graduate since most hospitals know new graduates require more training and mentorship, and also take time to become efficient at seeing patients. The most important thing to consider is to find a job with an appropriate salary for the cost of living in its city (you can look this up online) so that you can live comfortably. I would also make sure to ask about growth potential.

Location: This is one area you can control. As you would expect, vet hospitals in larger cities tend to offer higher salaries. These hospitals are in areas with higher costs of living, tend to have clientele with higher incomes, and usually are very busy. It will be important to look at housing options early so you can see if the higher salary allows you to live comfortably near the city or if commuting 20-30 minutes is a better option for you. By researching the area thoroughly, you can begin to see what your budget will look like and feel better about the offer provided by your future employer.

Type of practice: There is quite a range of starting salaries depending on the type of practice. As you can imagine, this variation can skew the statistics when you are trying to compare things. Small animal practices and emergency practices tend to offer higher salaries than equine, large animal, exotic/zoo, or mixed animal practices. Jobs in government or the private sector such as drug companies, pet food companies, etc tend to offer higher salaries as well as strong benefit packages. There will always be variance, but this trend has shown an increase over time as pet insurance increases in popularity, decreasing the financial burden on pet owners. Emergency medicine will tend to pay more to make up for the decreased work-life balance working nights, weekends, and holidays.

Internship: Salaries for internships are all posted on the VIRMP application website under each specific program. The salaries can vary from $18,000-$50,000. Veterinary colleges tend to fall to the lower end, while busy private practices are on the higher end. These are non-negotiable, but most internships will offer additional benefits for you such as paid health insurance, pet discounts, an all-expense paid trip to a vet conference, to name a few. If interested in pursuing advanced training, there are loan deferment options available to either postpone or reduce your monthly loan payments.

My best advice is to do your research based on where you want to live and the type of environment you wish to practice in. I like using websites such as Glass Door or good ole' Google when looking for averages in certain cities. Another option is to scroll through the AVMA website, which has a variety of job postings you can look at to get a better idea for your level of experience. Most will say, "new graduates welcome to apply" if they are open to hiring you.

Our field is proving to be an economically stable profession with steady increases in starting salaries for new graduates, as well as for each year you are out in practice. AVMA researchers found that from 2001-2016 the mean starting salary went from around $40,000 to more than $58,000. Remember that this is an average, inclusive of all jobs in veterinary medicine. When the AVMA looked at starting salaries in the different areas of practice, small animal exclusive vets had the highest starting average salary of around $71,462. Large animal exclusive vets were around $68,933. Mixed animal vets were around $62,327. Equine vets had the lowest first-year salary, which may be partly due to the need for internships, at $38,468. If pursuing an internship, the average starting salary was around $30,829.

I know none of us are drawn to veterinary medicine for the money, but there are some interesting growth trends with salary. The AVMA found that salaries are showing an increase of around 6% with each year you are out in practice. This is higher than inflation and cost of living increases, so I do feel this shows we have stability to count on as we pay off our debt. The Bureau of Labor Statistics reports a median salary for veterinarians of $88,770. It also reports the best paid veterinarians earn close to $161,070, while the lowest paid earn around $52,470. The AVMA found that vets in private practice average $124,768, while veterinarians employed by the federal government average $90,976. Corporate veterinarians average $117,000 per year. It was also found that board-certified specialists have average salaries exceeding $110,000.

Another factor to consider is that with owning your own practice, you can expect to earn a higher salary. Articles recently have been showing concern that younger veterinarians are shying away from owning a hospital. It is true that practice ownership means incurring more debt, however, over time you are building a revenue stream that far outpaces your associates. You will also have a business that you can sell in the future so you should not ignore this opportunity. The AVMA found a $40,000 annual income increase in practice ownership averaging a $120,000 salary. This range will of course still vary based on the size of the hospital you own, location of the practice, etc.

With all this talk about salary, I'm sure you are wondering now how easy it is to actually land a job. One positive is that the AVMA found in 2016 that more than half of U.S. households own a pet. This is a huge market for us, and another interesting fact is that 27% of these households did not even visit a veterinarian in 2016. This means we have a lot of work to do to communicate the importance of veterinary care to this untapped market. Despite the above percentage, there is a huge, growing demand for veterinarians. The Bureau of Labor Statistics projects there will be 14,400 new jobs in our field by 2026. Our job market is expected to grow by 18% as compared to 16% for other health occupations. This is a striking number and very exciting as our veterinary class sizes continue to increase. There are currently more jobs out there than applicants, which is good if you are in the market. It is important to consider that some locations will be in higher demand than others so it is worth broadening your search parameters in the beginning as you job hunt.

The last few decades have also shown a significant change in the veterinary job market. The time of independently owned veterinary hospitals is dwindling. There are plenty of reasons why, but it is important to realize this will cause differences within private practice because corporate medicine has started to take over. You will find a high proportion of hospitals are actually corporate owned by some of these well-known proprietors: V.C.A., Banfield, and N.V.A. to name a few.

There are definite differences between corporate and independent hospitals. Some benefits of corporate medicine to consider are standardized health care protocols, effective protocols already in place, economies of scale, the potential for a higher salary, and better benefits. The downside to corporate medicine is there may be more focus on your production in the hospital annually and less freedom to practice the medicine of your choice. This means you may not have much say in the day to day at your hospital or in influencing important decisions. I would consider this when you choose a hospital because you are in this environment every day so you want to pick somewhere you will be happiest.

I want you to start preparing early for the job hunt and take all of these factors into consideration. You can start thinking about where you want to look and what type of work culture you hope to find. It is very helpful to set up your external rotations wisely where you are visiting cities of interest or are spending time at practices you want to work at. You have few free moments in your senior year, so these externships provide you the opportunity to get face time with practices of interest. I want you to find your ideal job where you can be willing to stay for at least two to three years at a minimum. If you find you do not like your current job, it can end up hurting you in the end because you need to put down roots in order to build up a clientele. I have been at the same practice for five years, and it has provided me with a steady clientele where I am always busy with booked appointments. I absolutely love seeing the same patients and owners every day, and this is hands down my favorite part of the job.

3. TO INTERN OR NOT TO INTERN?

I had a serious internal debate in September of my senior year about whether to apply for an internship. I knew I wanted to be a doctor of small animals, but I was bogged down by how many decisions there were to make within this field alone. At thirteen, I really did not process there were veterinary neurologists or small animal emergency clinicians. I just thought you graduated from vet school and then got to take care of animals. As I progressed through school, I just got more and more confused about where my path was going to take me. I found that I really liked the idea of being a general practitioner but also had an interest in emergency medicine, neurology, and surgery. I wanted to keep my options open so I decided to apply for an internship.

I remember talking with different doctors about it, and it was almost across the board that the feedback I got was "If you do not want to specialize, then don't do an internship." I personally did not like that feedback. Do schools really think we are ready after just three classroom years and one clinical year? To be fair, I do not feel you can ever be ready. Let's compare us to human medicine for a minute. Every single new graduate has to complete an internship or advanced training program first to get them ready for their career. I do not feel a veterinary internship is for everyone, but the main benefit of an internship is that they are centered on consistent mentorship and growth of a new graduate. It is still possible to find a hospital that provides this straight out of school, but you definitely need to know what to ask and how to look (more on that later).

In 2018 there were 1401 internship positions available, and the numbers continue to rise. Internships had a match rate of 64% in 2018. I will say that not every internship program is created equal so you MUST do your research. This means you need to actually visit as many hospitals as possible and email with current interns to learn about their experiences so far with the program. You will then be able to compare programs better as what is said on the VIRMP or over the phone may not always be accurate. All of this will help you find the best fit for you and your future goals.

In order to apply for an internship, you will need to fill out an application on the VIRMP website. This website is helpful to look at if you are even just considering applying as they have information on the matching process, internship programs, principles of the selection process, application packets, and fees associated. Your application packet will be what each internship program reviews for every applicant, and it consists of a resume, personal statement, transcripts, and letters of reference. There are application deadlines and once submitted, the internship directors will review your packet and schedule phone interviews. The first interview helps the program to get to know you better, and then it is always best you try to make it for an in-person interview afterwards. I know some programs will not even consider you if you do not visit. The visit benefits you too because it allows you to see how the hospital operates, which gives you a chance to get to know the staff and current interns to form a first-hand impression of the working environment. You want to determine if the program is a good fit for you too.

You can find internship programs in both private practice and the university setting. I know I had heard that if you go to a university internship, you might have a better shot at a residency. However, I recently attended the first VIRMP conference and was happy to hear that most programs are looking for excellent references, strong academic standing, and well-rounded résumés, not necessarily putting higher weight on a university versus private practice internship. That being said, the vast majority of residency programs are in academia. Of the 372 residency positions, 321 are in institutions and 51 are in private practice. This is in contrast to internships where private practice had 1,044 internships in 2018, while institutions only had 357. If you are analyzing this data as I am, I feel the main advantage of matching at an institution is networking. You will have a better shot at getting to know the right people and working under doctors who may have strong connections at other institutions.

I am not going to lie to you and say your internship year is going to be smooth sailing. There are plenty of things to consider when making this decision. The important part of considering an internship is that it keeps your options open early on in your career when you are still trying to find your niche within veterinary medicine.

Pros of an Internship:

- <u>Mentorship:</u> Many programs are like a well-oiled machine and have been teaching new graduates for a long time. This means you will already have doctors willing to teach/train, daily rounds to attend, labs to grow your skills, and various other opportunities to support your growth over the year. This is something extremely hard to find in a first job so it is nice to know this is already built into a strong internship program.

- <u>Caseload:</u> Most hospitals that support an internship program will be very busy and tend to have more advanced cases than the average, smaller hospital. The patients will be triaged and worked up through emergency from the beginning or are sent as a referral from another hospital for advanced diagnostics and procedures. This allows you to see more variety than vet school and gives you confidence in managing a broad caseload. You become better equipped to handle these cases both as the primary and secondary doctor.

- <u>Time Management:</u> There will be days when there are eight triages waiting to be seen and an emergency surgery to be cut. This pressure pushes you to become more efficient earlier in your career seeing patients as well as teaching you how to delegate better to your staff.

- <u>Stress Management:</u> As you can imagine from all of the above, it is going to be a busy, long year. I remember some 16-hour days at the hospital when it was a busy emergency-filled day. I do believe this can teach you how to handle your stress better and earlier in your career by prioritizing, learning to say "no", and finding the best ways to blow off steam.

- Structure: Most internships have a rotating schedule that has a set structure to ensure you experience a variety of surgery, medicine, and emergency cases. Other benefits are that there will be rounds scheduled, so you have set times to pick other doctors' brains on your cases, allowing you opportunity to learn from one another. Internships tend to have formal reviews as well to provide you with feedback to help you grow throughout the year. There may be other things set in place such as monthly meetings with the director or a mentor, reviewing of your records, morbidity and mortality (M&M) rounds, in hospital continuing education, etc. This first year out may be the only time you get to experience educational structure after vet school.

Cons of an Internship:
- Hours: Unfortunately, your hours will not be the associate hours you longed for while in school. Some internships have you working 60-80 hour work weeks. This will vary from program to program and is something to consider as you talk with current interns. I have heard nightmares of some hospitals requiring you to stay on site for 72 hours straight. I was lucky in that we were only scheduled 42-45 hours per week with no on-call shifts during my internship. However, what kept me late was writing my records after a shift (sometimes 2-5 hours after), but this got better as I became more efficient. You will want to compare what your scheduled hours are per week between each internship, which is the time frame you are actually seeing patients, to how long after shifts

interns stay on average (ask them!), as well as on-call requirements.

- **Salary:** The VIRMP website will have the salary, benefits, etc listed for each program. The salary for an internship will be lower than if you were getting your first job as an associate. This is in part due to the time taken to teach and grow you. *Side note:* My comment to this con is that I feel you can make a higher salary after an internship, so this may even out the lower "salary hit" over time. This is because many people see internship training as equivalent to approximately three years out in private practice. In addition to the case-load and experience, you will be much more confident and efficient after just one year.

- **Case Responsibility:** This varies from hospital to hospital in how much primary case responsibility you will have daily. Some offer complete primary case responsibility with doctors always there to help you, while others have you follow a doctor around similar to when you were in school. You may not have as much primary case responsibility when working directly with specialists, but the benefit is you get to see how they manage cases. Some hospitals will provide a mixture of both. Just remember, you went through your senior year without much case responsibility so it is important to find a good balance here when comparing hospitals as primary case responsibility helps to grow your confidence.

- **Hands-on Experience:** This also varies based on the hospital environment. If the hospital you are looking at has residents, they may be taking most experiences away from you with regards to surgery, procedures, etc. Specialty hospitals will offer fewer hands-on surgical opportunities due to the fact that the majority of procedures being performed there need a board-certified surgeon. If you are looking at a private practice that is an emergency/general practice, you most likely will have more hands-on opportunities because the caseload and hospital structure will allow you to perform these surgeries.

I do not regret my decision to do an internship. Some may call me biased now that I am the internship director at my hospital, but I actually see it as an extension of just how passionate I am about internships. I believe a well-chosen internship helps you decide what you want to do with your career. At the end of my internship year, I decided I was interested in too many areas to specialize. I opted to become a well-rounded general practitioner who also practices emergency medicine. Since I was exposed to a variety of cases in just one year, I felt extremely confident moving forward to this next chapter. I have felt prepared for the caseload and can see my continued growth each year. My current passion is abdominal ultrasound, and I love how I am able to improve and grow this skill through continuing education and practice. You do not need to specialize to advance your skills.

I truly believe there is a need for more general practice doctors in private practice to take it to the next level through an internship and continuing education. There are only a small percentage of clients who can afford referral to see a specialist, so we need to be able to offer high quality medicine at a variety of price points. I know some general practitioners that refer when the medicine gets complicated. I want to remind you that specialists were not as readily available decades ago depending on where you lived, and veterinary medicine revolved around picking up a book to figure it out. I am thankful veterinary medicine has reached a higher standard of care as a whole, but general practitioners and specialists do need to work together. It is important for us as doctors to be able to screen pets appropriately for disease, start management of said disease, and know when it is best for a patient to see a specialist based on the outcome or how the case is evolving. Not only will this allow veterinary medicine to adapt and survive in an ever-changing economy, but it will also give you continued job satisfaction to manage these difficult cases. You will begin to build a client base that trusts and values your skills, and I believe this is one of the keys to preventing burnout as a doctor.

Outside of pursuing a residency, emergency medicine is one career path I feel strongly benefits from an internship. Most emergency veterinary job postings advertise that they want candidates with an internship or at least two years of emergency experience. There is a steep learning curve to becoming a well-rounded emergency clinician from being able to stabilize a STAT with confidence to performing a GDV surgery to managing a very sick patient overnight with multiple diseases. On top of that, you may have 25 sick pets walk in that night with 10 hospitalized patients to manage as well. Even five years out, this scenario gives me heart palpitations and that can be a typical emergency shift. It is difficult to have that confidence after four years of school, and you do not want to find yourself in a hospital working all by yourself with only a doctor on call. Emergency clinicians are in high demand, and I can guarantee you that you will be offered a higher salary after an internship than you would upon graduation. I feel that more importantly, you will be able to grow as a young doctor in a more structured way with less heartache over the mistakes you made as you were learning.

If your eyes are set on a residency, it is important to be prepared for potentially two to three internships before you land a residency position. Residences have become more competitive over the years. Despite the fact that the number of internship positions is growing, the number of residency positions has remained static for the last 20 years. In 2018, there were 372 residency positions available with an average match rate of 30% for applicants, a one in three chance of landing a residency. Despite this, the number of students applying for a residency is growing making it extremely competitive. This can be disconcerting, but you have to be realistic. It is important to set yourself up with a backup plan if you find you are not matching with a program.

If you want to pursue one of the more competitive residencies, then your best bet is to aim for an internship in academia. The more competitive residencies are radiology, cardiology, ophthalmology, and zoo/exotic medicine. This is in part due to the fact that these specialties do not have a lot of residency programs. Another factor to consider is which specialties have the most applicants. In 2018, these specialties were radiology, emergency medicine/critical care, equine surgery, small animal medicine, and small animal surgery. Interestingly, the residencies with the highest number of programs in private practice were emergency medicine/critical care and surgery. My best advice is to honestly try to look for the best fit for what you want out of your year and think about how it will get you to your goals. If your eyes are set on a residency, it will be important to network from day one and demonstrate a strong work ethic throughout your internship.

4. THE JOB HUNT

I still remember the fourth year scramble like it was yesterday. NAVLE and internship match results were back. This news left the majority of my class, who didn't apply for an internship, antsy to find their first real job. Some of my classmates were lucky enough to just head home to the family practice, but the majority had the dreaded, BUT exciting, job hunt ahead of them. There are a lot of factors that go into your job search. It can be quite daunting in the beginning because there are actually a lot more positions than applicants at this time. This is great news for our profession, but it also means you may need to be flexible in some of the areas mentioned next in order to find your ideal job.

The first factor to consider is location. People will tend to gravitate towards the bigger cities like New York City, Los Angeles, Atlanta, Washington D.C., etc. The larger cities will always have more hospitals but with this brings more competition. You have to find ways to stand out from other applicants; a competitive edge will help you land a job. The smaller cities or towns will have fewer positions but tend to have fewer applicants. With this in mind, my advice is to broaden your search initially so that you can see what is out there. It may help to find smaller towns near big cities. This allows you to compare job opportunities and will ultimately end up increasing the number of positions you can consider. Your first job is the most important one because it will begin to mold your career and give you the tools you need to become successful. Thoroughly evaluate your job prospects to see if you will get what you need from that particular hospital. In the end, it is not about being in your dream city initially; it is about career preparation.

The second factor to consider is the type of practice. You will want to decide if you are strictly going to work with small animal vs. mixed animal vs. exotic vs. large animal vs. equine. If you apply for a mixed animal practice but have no interest in large animal medicine, you may still come across instances where you have to work on a goat that comes in for a dystocia because you are the only doctor there or are on call. This will be important to discuss with your future employer, as this can impact your stress level if there are species you do not feel comfortable working on.

It is also important to consider what hours the hospital is open. This could impact your expected hours and schedule to include on-call hours, weekend shifts, holidays, or working later such as up to 8-10 p.m. Hospitals that are open 24/7 can end up keeping you at work past your scheduled shift some days due to the caseload. You may be busier or see a higher majority of sick patients that require hospitalization. This will expose you to different aspects of medicine but can impact your work-life balance. By determining the types of animals you want to work with and the practice type, this will influence what patients you see and how long your shifts will be. These are factors to consider if you would like to work in an environment with steadier hours.

The third factor to consider is your benefits package. When I signed my first contract, I had no idea what was included in a typical benefits package for a veterinarian. Granted, I chose to do an internship so there was minimal negotiation, but when I landed my associate job I had no frame of reference for what could be offered. I have been in the same hospital for five years now so I opened up a conversation with my fellow classmates to see what they have come across with regards to competitive benefits as a comparison. For your reference, my classmates who helped me with this information are practicing small animal medicine all over the country.

Your benefits package consists of a variety of factors: paid time off (this can include personal, sick, and C.E. time), a budget for continuing education, retirement account plans, and health insurance to name a few. I have compiled some of this data for you to use as a baseline on what to expect in your first five years out of practice. As you progress through your career, these may improve further with negotiation, but the goal here is to give you a frame of reference.

P.T.O/Paid time off: P.T.O. includes the days you are allowed to take for personal time. I found as a general consensus that most practices offer a blanket number that is to be used for vacation, personal, and sick days. Very few veterinarians are offered a separation in days (a few did get offered ten vacation days with five sick days for example). The lowest amount of paid time off I saw was five to seven days, which was typically for an internship, with the most being fifteen days. Some practices offer you more paid time off as you stay at the hospital, such as going from ten to fifteen days after two years, or accruing an additional day per year until you reach a certain number. Another aspect of paid time off to consider is that if you are going to make a base salary with production, you will need to ask if your paid time off is included in your production. This can be confusing to understand without an example. If you take one week off in August, then you will be paid a salary during your vacation week, but technically you are not producing for the hospital. That time off will cause you to potentially have a "negative production month" because you only worked fifteen days instead of your average twenty. Some hospitals have this in their contract, so you need to understand that the month you are on vacation you may not receive a bonus check, a check you would normally receive if you worked the entire time.

It is good to know that when it comes to negotiation on P.T.O., you do have options. Speaking from experience, I can say that my twelve vacation days do not always feel like enough. Time off from work is very important as it gives you time to decompress, and unfortunately, our profession does not have the benefits an office job can offer. My husband has unlimited P.T.O., which still baffles me because I am sure there are people who take advantage of this luxury. I often have to work the day before or after holidays because my hospital is always open. This means you may not always get the entire week off like your significant other gets around a holiday. By keeping all of this in mind, it allows you to compare offers and see what can be negotiated as well as what is important to you. EVERYTHING is negotiable! I hope that over time practice owners will start to value the importance of paid time off more than they currently do, to allow us time with our families and to enjoy a good work-life balance.

C.E./Continuing Education Days: This can vary per hospital, but on average I saw anywhere between one day to one week devoted to continuing education. The most common amount of time off was three to five days, which often provides enough time to attend a conference. It is important to have a few days devoted separately to C.E. because you need at least three to five days to attend a large conference. This will account for travel time to and from the conference, as well as give you ample time to enjoy the lectures. If you are looking to grow a skill, such as with ultrasound or acupuncture, this can require more time off than the average. Most states require fifteen to twenty hours of continuing education to be completed each year so knowing your state requirements will help you to negotiate this as well. It can be difficult to get over twenty hours without attending a major conference each year.

C.E. Budget: I found the budget offered to most veterinarians appeared fairly consistent with the majority being between $1,000-2,500. I personally feel that if you want to attend a larger conference outside of your city, then you need at least $2,500. This budget will be needed to cover your conference registration, transportation costs, meals, and hotel, so be sure to clarify what this budget specifically covers. When I went to Western in Las Vegas a few years ago, it was easily $1,500. Conferences are a fun time to reminisce with old classmates, mingle with other veterinarians, and experience a new city. I value this as an important perk in negotiations so work hard for an appropriate amount.

Retirement Account: I was thrilled to find out that the majority of my classmates have retirement plans offered through work with matching options. Examples of these plans are a 401K or IRA. The differences between the two are that a 401K is offered through an employer and allows you to put more money into it annually ($18,500), whereas an IRA is opened individually with a lower amount allowed into the account annually ($6,000, but this value can depend on the type of IRA). Typically, IRA's are offered by smaller veterinary hospitals. You can deduct the amount you put into the accounts off your taxes each year, as it is tax-free until you withdraw it later, so a 401K offers you a larger tax deduction lowering your taxable income.

The best perk of these plans is when employers match a certain percentage of what you put into the account each year. Most employers are offering a 3-5% match, so this means that if you put 3% of your salary into the account annually, they will then add an additional 3% to the account for you (totaling up to 6% of your salary per year). This ends up being extra money you would not otherwise receive each year. Pay attention to plan details, as some employers will offer a match, but if you leave the job within one to two years, you may only get 50% of what they added to your account. However, you will always keep what you put into your account no matter what. Most jobs have you 100% vested after working there a certain period of time, which means everything your employer contributes to your account becomes yours even once you leave the job. I would pay attention to this in your contract as most jobs reward those who stay longer, so it is all the more reason to read the fine print to know these details ahead of time.

Insurance: You will be offered a variety of insurance options. Unfortunately, smaller veterinary hospitals may not be able to provide you with health insurance or will offer to pay a part of the cost (50% for example). With the rising cost of health care, I find coverage by the hospital to be an excellent perk if offered. My basic health insurance with dental per month is around $365, and this amount adjusts slightly each year based on the market. This cost can add up, and that doesn't include the cost of paying your deductible, which can be as high as $5,000 if you get injured or severely ill. Some companies offer to pay a portion of your deductible too, and offer great health insurance benefits like dental, vision, life, and short-term disability. If you know you will need health insurance outside of your spouse's company plan, you will want to consider a way to negotiate for this as it can end up being a $4-5,000 out of pocket expense annually. It is important to compare what the hospital is offering to other insurance plans too, as their offered plan may not cover everything you need. I feel at minimum employers should be offering health insurance, whether the cost is completely or partially covered. Dental and vision insurance tends to be low, about $30-50 per month, and can be added on personally if you opt for it.

The fourth factor to consider is mentorship. In my opinion, this is one of the most important things to look for and is often overlooked. From my own experience, it ranks highest in importance. As a new graduate, I believe your first year out of school is the most important for setting the stage for your career. I still remember how every appointment or emergency I saw my first few months filled me with questions, and I was so thankful to have a supportive group of veterinarians there to guide me. We all get busy but having my colleagues set aside time to talk me through a daunting case in the beginning meant so much to me, and it can be a game-changer in many instances. It takes time to build your confidence as a doctor so finding a strong support system is your key to getting there. When a STAT patient comes in, I want you to be in a hospital with doctors willing to guide you through these times of stress, as these cases push you out of your comfort zone. Otherwise, your growth will be slower paced because it is ultimately driven by your exposure, caseload, and developing comfort level with difficult cases.

There are a few ways to know if you are going to be working in a supportive learning environment. Look at the range in ages of the doctors at the hospital. If it is fairly spread out, it shows the hospital is used to accepting new graduates and growing them within the practice. The number of doctors can play a role in the mentorship experience as well because if it is a three doctor practice, this probably means there will be another associate and yourself on the books routinely to allow for the other doctor's time off. This makes it more challenging to get 1-on-1 help if they are busy seeing appointments too. My personal opinion is that a larger practice (5+ doctors) is most ideal for a new graduate. Watch how doctors and staff interact on the floor to see if things seem collaborative.

When talking with your future boss, you should ask questions about what they do to help you in your first few months. For example, some clinics will start you out with longer appointment times (40 minutes to 1 hour instead of 30 minutes) while others have you see appointments every 15 to 20 minutes. Longer appointments can be extremely helpful because not only are you working through your medicine and client communication, but you are also learning how to navigate their hospital software, write records, and delegate to staff. It is also helpful if you are paired up with an experienced veterinary assistant or technician so they can show you the ropes. Lastly, some hospitals will have a senior doctor review random samplings of your records, which is helpful to check your drug calculations, medical advice, treatment plan, etc in the beginning. This helps to ensure your medical record is adequate in case of a potential medical board review, as what is written in the real world is much different than in vet school.

The main thing to confirm when assessing mentorship is to determine if you are just going to be another body seeing patients or if the hospital is an environment where doctors grow within the hospital and appear supported. You will figure this out by asking how they grow you professionally, whether through performance reviews, scheduled rounds, assigned mentors, etc. I hate to hear when new graduates leave their first job after just one year. Your first few years out of school are so important, as they provide you with the foundation for success. It also takes time to build up a clientele, and this is extremely important to improving your salary, as it means you will be seeing more patients than when you first started out. You want to find an environment where you can see yourself staying for a few years in order to get the most out of your experience and that particular hospital. You don't want to end up somewhere where you are the solo doctor on a busy Saturday, or where you are left in the surgical suite while the other two doctors are busy seeing patients at the other end of the hospital. If you do find yourself in an unsuitable work environment, I want you to know you can find a practice that is right for you. These supportive work environments DO exist and are extremely important to find when you are a novice doctor. Once you have experience under your belt, you can feel confident in any environment.

The fifth and final factor to consider is salary. I have already provided salary ranges you can expect, both as a new graduate and with experience. Your salary will always vary based on the location of the practice, your experience level, the status of the economy, and competition for hiring. The most important consideration is that it is appropriate in relation to the cost of living in that particular location. Salary options you may see among practices include a base salary by itself, production/commission based salary, and a base salary plus a percentage of your production, called "pro-sal."

A base salary alone has many advantages when first starting out. It can be difficult to produce as a veterinarian when you are new. You do not have a solid client base yet, and you will tend to be less efficient in the first six months while you get your feet wet. I can compare my production from my first year to my fourth year, and it is almost 2-2.5 times more now. By receiving a set salary for the year, you have a little less stress over "making your numbers" each month. You want to be able to focus on the skills that will make you a better doctor so that you can earn more over time. Production can cause un-needed stress when you already have a lot on your plate in your first year.

When you are offered a base salary plus production, it typically means you are offered a lower salary but get bonus checks either monthly, quarterly, or annually for a percentage of what you earn above your break-even point. You still have to make a minimum amount of production per month in order to receive a bonus. The percentage you receive can vary depending on if it is a medication, doctor service, or prescription food. It will be important to ask what percentage of production you will get for each item, as this is another area that may be able to be negotiated. As you see more patients, there is a huge benefit to having production as part of your salary. It is not that we "sell more" but more about seeing more patients, being more confident in your medicine, and having regular clients that support you and your recommendations. By always practicing high quality medicine, you will have better productivity. The benefit of production is that it is motivating and makes you feel better if you have to stay late for a procedure or surgery that keeps you after your shift. I do feel this is a great option after one to two years of experience, or it can be an option for a new graduate if you feel comfortable with this mindset.

A salary that is strictly based off production or commission can be difficult for a new graduate. You do not know this yet, but the winter months (December-February) tend to be slower in many hospitals. Therefore, you may make less or no production during these months. This can vary but is important to keep in mind if you strictly make production because you may not receive a paycheck in those months or make a lower paycheck than you are used to receiving. This will be important to know so that you can budget throughout the year for these times. I have not come across this option often, but it is important to know as it may be offered. I do not feel it is a good choice for a newer veterinarian.

When comparing offers, it is important to consider how much pressure you want to feel with regards to production. If you want to be able to learn with lower stress, a salary is the best option. If you already feel very confident in veterinary medicine and perhaps are moving to an area where you know a lot of people, a base salary with production may be for you. I also want you to know what kind of salary growth you can expect over time. If your future employer offers you X salary, ask how raises are distributed over time so that you will know what to expect. It may also be worthwhile to see if you can transition from a salary your first year to a base salary with production the next year once you are ready. Everything is negotiable, so my best advice is to find the offer that suits you and to know what you can expect from that practice over time.

So, where are we? You now have a list of hospitals that you want to apply to, as well as a comparison of the factors we have discussed in the previous sections to guide your decisions. Armed with this information you can now rank your prospects to streamline your job-hunt. You have more ammo to evaluate the pros and cons while you decide what is most important to you as well as what hospital will provide the best experience to meet your goals. This information will help you keep your thoughts organized and allow you to dive head first into the interview process.

5. THE APPLICATION PROCESS, INTERVIEWING FOR YOUR FIRST JOB, AND NAVIGATING YOUR CONTRACT

Now that you have narrowed down your job search, you can sit back and relax right!? NOPE! Now it is time to get your resume adjusted and sent off to the hospitals you are interested in. You can apply to any hospital with an open job offer, but I do encourage you to also apply to any hospital you are interested in because you never know when they may be open to hiring. Once your resume is sent, the waiting period begins. It can take hospitals some time to get back to you, but a good rule of thumb is to check in with them after one week if you have not heard from them yet. It shows you are interested and also helps you stay on track so you are not stuck waiting, which leads to missed opportunities.

Where to begin? Are you feeling paralyzed because you have no idea how to actually design or adjust your resume? You more than likely have something from your vet school application packet, and then you never thought about it again. To start the process, I strongly recommend finding a contact in your Academic Affairs or Student Life department. There is usually someone who specializes in helping students through this process since you cannot stay in vet school forever. They may have example resumes or templates you can use to make the process less daunting. There are many websites now that have templates where you fill in the information, and then it gets formatted automatically. AVMA and AAHA also have templates and resources you can peruse as well. I remember I had a lecture in third year about resume building, which was very helpful. However, at the time clinics were hanging over my head so I didn't immediately jump into adjusting my resume. Looking back, I should have started the process sooner, so that it was not so overwhelming. I personally procrastinated until the last minute to make my resume prior to the intern match deadline causing unnecessary stress in my fourth year. I hope every veterinary school helps you out professionally, but if they do not, find someone who can help you because this may not be something that comes easy. You have to be able to sell yourself on paper first.

Your resume should be updated so that it includes only relevant veterinary work. No one wants to read about your three restaurant jobs during your summers in undergrad. However, it may be helpful to highlight in your cover letter your "client service" background with a little ode to these positions, but I recommend keeping the bulk of your resume focused on your future career path. In the last four years, I have read over 100 new graduate resumes for our internship program, and I have learned what draws my eye in. I have also learned some no-no's that have quickly become resume pet peeves.

I'll start by breaking down some of the sections you should include in your resume. I have noticed that the formatting of resumes is getting "trendier" so it may be fun to look up some examples online to see if there are any unique updates you can add to your resume to stand apart from the crowd. Just make sure to keep it professional and easy to read.

Cover Letter: You should ALWAYS write a unique cover letter for each job. There are tons of formats out there, but the main objective is to show you have researched the hospital, outline what you like about it, explain your unique self, and what you specifically can bring to the job they have posted. Here, you want to highlight all of the specific areas that make you the best candidate for the job. It is almost like a prequel and summary of your resume to allow whoever is reading it to feel like they have gotten to know you better. Resumes can be a little bland so this is where you can really shine!

Contact Information: The top portion of your resume includes your name and below that, you can have up to two addresses with your contact information: left is your current address and to the right is your permanent address. If you will only have one address during the application process, then keep it simple. I would include your cell phone and email address as well. If your email address is not appropriate, please for the love of vet med, get a temporary Gmail account. No one will take you seriously if your email address is princessfluffy2021@gmail.com (I made that email address up so I hope it doesn't exist! And no, it's not my email.)

Objective: What are you looking for? This can be as simple as "To obtain a position as a full-time small animal veterinarian." I noticed recently that some of the latest resumes have a professional summary then an objective, but that is up to you if you want to include both. Keep it short, as length belongs in the cover letter.

Education: This section includes both your veterinary and undergraduate studies. There are mixed opinions about putting your G.P.A. in this section. If you are more "street smart" than "book smart" as they say, you might want to highlight other strengths and not list your G.P.A. if it could be seen as a detractor. A good rule of thumb is that if your G.P.A. is less than a 3.5, then do not list it. You can also highlight added electives you took that may help to put you ahead of other applicants.

Clinical Experience: This should be the largest section of your resume. Include all relevant externships and veterinary jobs. You will want to state the length of time you were at each location. I would detail everything you can relative to the experience you received at each job, any hands-on experiences, and teaching opportunities to highlight the value of your experiences.

Skills: This can include computer software you have used (such as Cornerstone, E-film, Avimark), your familiarity with various lab equipment (such as coagulation machine, etc), veterinary equipment (such as surgical laser, endoscope, ultrasound, etc), and other skills (ability to perform a blood transfusion, nutritional assessment, etc). If you have done multiple surgeries or performed high volume spay/neuter, then include the number of patients as well to highlight your surgical proficiency. This area is meant to show off your unique experiences to set you apart.

Activities: This is where you put a combination of both undergraduate and veterinary experiences outside of class and clinics. It is meant to highlight your participation in extra-curriculars to show you are well rounded and highlights any leadership positions you have held. I included things such as my memberships in veterinary clubs, leadership positions within my sorority, and my Purina student representative job. I elaborated on the leadership, education, and delegation skills that I gained from these activities.

Honors & Awards: Here you can put any scholarships you received throughout undergraduate and veterinary school. If you received any special awards for your service or leadership, I would place them here as well. This highlights how other people have perceived the qualities within you that you are advertising and will strengthen your other sections.

Professional Affiliations: In this section, you can list the professional veterinary groups you are a member of such as AVMA or SAVMA. You can also list any state affiliations if you are already a member.

Continuing Education: This section is where you list the major conferences you have attended or any courses outside of school you have completed (such as Fear Free Certification).

My hope is that the above sections provide a great starting point for organizing yourself on paper. There may be other sections you add in based on your unique experiences, or a particular template you find. The goal is to appear professional and highlight your unique attributes in order to stand out from the other candidates.

There are a few areas of a resume that really stand out to me. My favorite section is the cover letter. I feel like I get to know the person better through their style of writing. When I review the resume, I like to look at the variety of experiences that have been pursued to show well-roundedness. The other area I really pay attention to is the activities section to highlight any leadership roles. As a veterinarian, it is very important to be a confident leader. You will be explaining to your clients what to do regarding their pets' health every single day, and you need to communicate well with your staff. Leadership shows you can communicate with a variety of people and have learned the necessary skills to "get the job done." On the other hand, the biggest pet peeve of mine is spelling errors, or if the applicant has not researched the hospital prior to applying. There is no excuse for a spelling error nowadays when using software with Spellcheck, and the internet makes researching hospitals very easy. I want to see an enthusiastic, engaged applicant, who appears well rounded.

Ok, resume paralysis cured! Now submit that application already!! Once the hospital has read through your cover letter and resume, most will start with a phone interview. Depending on the size of the hospital, it may be a human resources staff member, practice manager, or hospital owner who reaches out to you first. The initial phone interview will center on why you are applying to work there and the content of your resume. Then, typically, an in-person interview will follow. When you arrive at the hospital, please dress professionally - business attire is best. Most likely, you will start your day with a hospital tour followed by shadowing a doctor or two so that you can meet the staff and experience a typical workday. This is not a test of your medicine, but rather your personality and how you engage with the staff members. I recommend introducing yourself to everyone you come in contact with because you want to appear engaged and friendly. The candidates who stand out the most are pleasant to every employee, engaged in the flow of the day, and are helpful by offering to restrain animals for an example. I know it will not be your job to do so necessarily, but it shows you are not "above" any tasks and that you want to have a good rapport with the staff.

Just remember, your working interview is as much for you as it is for the hospital. They know you are about to graduate, and they are already prepared to grow you medically. The main focus of the working interview is to see if you can blend in with the personalities of the hospital and fit in as a member of the team. You want to determine if you can see yourself working there. Do you feel like you could spend 40+ hours a week at this hospital? Be sure to work through the list you made earlier outlining the top factors that make a job attractive to you. How many of these factors does the hospital possess? As I said before, mentorship should be your top priority. Set yourself up with a positive learning environment. You need to be able to actually see yourself in the job before signing the contract. If you cannot, then it may not be a good fit. Never settle!

Reviewing your first contract can be a daunting process. Congrats, by the way! It is not uncommon for a contract to be 10+ pages long, and have legal jargon that many people struggle to understand. It is important to read through the entire contract thoroughly, and if there are any sections you are unsure about, I recommend having someone close to you review it as well. There are lawyers, labor relations' attorneys, who specialize in contracts if you want a professional opinion. A lawyer will always be preferable.

The contract will cover a variety of topics, and the details will allow you to understand what is expected of you, and will outline what the hospital is offering you. The contract will usually include the list of duties you are expected to perform during your job. It will specify your start date, length of the contract, and termination policy. Most contracts will auto-renew on the same day each year. It will include the specified amount of hours you work per week as well as their holiday policies, on-call expectations, etc. Your salary will be listed, and there will be a benefits section that will include paid time off, C.E. days, and benefits allowance. There will be a section regarding your non-compete and confidentiality agreement. If you were to violate anything on the contract, there will be a section on what to expect with regards to legal action. You will need to go through each section and determine what areas are most important to you as well as flag anything that may seem unfair or unclear given this is your first job.

Licensing: I feel every employer should cover the cost of these in your contract because they are requirements to practice medicine. This section will either be included in a benefits budget lump sum (for example: $6,000 to cover licensing, insurance, continuing education, etc), or each license will have a separate description on how it is covered. Once you graduate, you will have annual state licensing, maybe a privilege license tax, dues for your AVMA membership, and personal liability insurance. DEA registration is another license you will need and is renewed every 3 years. These costs can total around $787 for your licensing and insurance, and your DEA license is $731 every 3 years (as of 2019). I mention these to you because you may not realize you have these additional expenses per year.

Non-compete: As I researched non-compete clauses, I found a lot of variability. This clause is describing the area you cannot practice in for a specified amount of time after you leave the job. The reason employers have these clauses is to protect their business and clientele. This will be determined either by miles (driving distance from your hospital to the next) or air miles (straight line out from the hospital forming a circumference you cannot practice in). Air miles cover more distance and therefore will push you farther out of a city, so be sure to clarify. In larger cities, some non-competes will only mention nearby hospitals or zip codes you cannot practice in. The longer you are in a job, the larger and longer your non-compete clause may become. There are restrictions on these by law and legal precedent, so if it seems inappropriate, you can always double check if it is enforceable. Remember once the specified time frame is over, you can go back to practicing anywhere. My best advice is to look at a map with your hospital in the center to visualize the size of the non-compete so you can assess if it is fair. It will help you to see what your options are to avoid a 45-minute commute if the job doesn't work out after a year.

As boring as a contract reads, you need to analyze each section thoroughly. Ask for clarification if you are unsure about a section. Always make sure you agree with the starting work date and confirm that the salary and benefits match what you were told you originally. There will be some portions of your contract you will want to do some research on to ensure they are fair. If changes are made, make sure they are initialed by both parties on the signed document.

Now that you have reviewed the contract, it is time to talk negotiations. There will be some areas of the contract an employer sees as set-in-stone, and others you can discuss further to figure out your options. Asking may be the only way you can figure this out. As we discussed earlier, it is good to prioritize the top items that are most important to you and make sure you are happy with how they are addressed in your contract. I would also see if there are terms explaining your benefits over time if you decide to stay on with the practice for a few years. It is helpful to know what you can expect regarding your salary growth, if you get more paid time off over time, an opportunity for a retirement account with employee match, and so on. You want to be clear on the contract renewal process, so you know when to negotiate each year.

This is your one and only chance to set up the contract as you see fit. Once you know what you want to change in your contract, it is best to put it into writing and then submit it to your future employer. Even if you are doing this in person, remember to ask for the changes, and then be quiet. It never hurts to ask for what you want, and you should be slightly uncomfortable with what you are asking for. Statistically speaking, we all undervalue ourselves, and this can make us poor negotiators. You need to be able to confidently ask for what you want, and then give your employer time to think about your offer. Otherwise, you might start hedging and talk the offer down out of anxiety.

They can always say no or counter your offer.

At the end of the day, you do have to be somewhat flexible because it is your first job, and you have yet to prove yourself. You may not get everything you want right away, but you need to feel you have at least been awarded your top priorities. You want to protect yourself, and not sell yourself short. You have the next year to learn as well as prove your worth so that you can continue to build your career through future negotiations.

6. FINANCIAL OVERVIEW

There is no better feeling than signing the official contract for your first veterinary job. You can now start to plan for graduation since you know your future location, cost of living, salary, and start date. Planning early is important so you can set yourself up for success financially.

The first step is to choose a smart living situation. Figure out your monthly budget. The best way is to find a website that will give you your bi-weekly salary with taxes taken out. There are payroll calculators online that you can use to help you calculate this amount. Personally, I feel that your mortgage or rent shouldn't be more than 25% of your monthly post-tax income. This will give you some extra wiggle room financially to start paying off your loans and begin saving. Don't forget to include other housing expenses too such as utilities, repairs, etc. Compare living near the hospital to a 20-minute commute. If you can save $200 bucks a month with a short commute, this may be worth it because that is an extra $2,400 per year you can use elsewhere. Since this is your first job, you want to avoid as much financial stress as possible. It can take some time to get your budget and financial plans figured out.

Now that you have your housing expenses laid out, it is time to figure out your loan repayment options. The choice that works best for you will depend on your salary and the debt you carry. Remember, you will not be paying off $150,000 quickly so try not to let the total stress you out. The best strategy is to figure out the amount you can comfortably afford monthly while also being able to save money for other important things such as buying a house, investing in the stock market, etc. The key is to choose from the different loan repayment plans to find the one that works best for your situation. You can always change your plan if it isn't working for you after a few months.

There are three common general loan repayment plans out there, and you would be well-advised to work with your specific lender or a loan counselor to determine the best plan for you. You will find that some of these common plans may not be ideal for your specific situation, as the choice can depend largely on the total cash amount and number of loans you have. You will want to focus on paying your higher interest loans off first. There may be options to refinance your loans to get a lower interest rate so it is worth looking into this. Sometimes you can also get all of your loans lumped together into one consolidated loan with one monthly payment, though it may or may not be "worth it" in your situation. If you choose to pursue an internship or advanced training, do not forget you can get your loan amount reduced or deferred during your training.

Standard Repayment Plan: This plan is a fixed monthly payment amount that will allow you to pay off your loans within a certain time frame, typically 10 to 30 years. This plan usually allows you to pay less over time when compared to the other plans.

Graduated Repayment Plan: This plan will start with lower payments at first that will then increase over time (usually every two years) until you reach an amount that allows you to pay your loans off within 10-30 years. This plan may have you pay more over time than the standard repayment plan but gives you financial flexibility when you are first starting out.

Income Based Repayment Plan: There are a few different types of income-based repayment plans (IBR vs. ICR vs. PAYE vs. REPAYE), and the specifics of each plan are best explained by your lender or a loan counselor. These plans will take a certain percentage (usually around 10-15%) of your income to pay off your loans. Your loan payments will be recalculated each year and are based on your updated income and family size. Know it will be important to submit your documentation annually, as if you are late, the interest that has accrued will get compounded into your new premium. If you are married and file joint taxes, then your spouse's income will also be used in the calculation, which will make your payments higher than when you are filing as a single payer. To use this plan, you usually need a higher debt to income ratio. This is a good option if you are going to do an internship with potential for a residency so that your payments increase as your salary grows. Typically during your internship and residency, your payments can be as low as $0, however your loans continue to accrue interest during this time. In addition, after 20 years, these programs typically "forgive" your loans. The remaining balance that is forgiven after 20 years is then taxable as income, so if this is your plan, it is important to start saving for that giant tax-year early.

There are a few strategies you can utilize to pay off your student debt faster. For example, when you choose your repayment plan, it can be helpful to pay above your minimum payment (even if just a small amount), as it can go directly toward your loan principal. Make sure to read your loan terms, as some apply the added payment to interest first. If you ever come across extra money such as with an inheritance, lottery winning, or bonus I would strongly recommend using that money, or a large percentage of it, toward paying off your loans. I know it is tempting to buy that new car you have been eyeing, but paying off your loans sooner will reduce the interest on top of your loan amount that adds up over time.

It can be easy to get tunnel vision when you first graduate, as we all want to pay off our loans as quickly as possible. You do not want to focus all of your extra money each month on your loans because you also need to prioritize buying a house, saving for retirement, and having some savings in case of an emergency. I know at first this can seem hard to swallow when all you feel is the weight of your student debt, but remember, you can increase your monthly loan payments over time as you earn more money. These loans are not going to go away quickly (I am still holding out for that mega million lottery ticket myself). You also need to think about your short and long-term financial goals. It is important to stash away a small amount each month in a savings account and over time increase that amount as your salary grows. A savings plan gives you added security so do not forgo this important safety factor.

The best way to start saving for retirement is with a 401K or IRA. These accounts allow you to pull money out of your paycheck either pre-tax or taxed based on the account you choose, and most of the time you do not even miss it. This money is then managed by an outside party and invested in the stock market so it will continue to grow over time. The sooner you start a retirement savings account, the better. Your early to mid-'20s is ideal. There are statistics out there that show if you invest $10,000 when you are 25, assuming a 5-8% annual rate of return, this can become $217,000 by the time you reach 65. If you wait 10 more years to invest this same amount, it will only be worth $101,000 at 65. By investing early, you are capitalizing on the growth potential of compounding interest. Your employer may also provide you with a match, which becomes extra money added to these accounts, in addition to the salary that you will receive annually.

Outside of a retirement account, there are many other types of savings accounts you can open. These include money market accounts, index funds, and other financial products. Some companies will help you manage your money for free or a small fee once you open up an account with them. You can also find apps that help you save in ways that you won't even notice the money is missing. I recommend talking to a financial advisor (or a savings-savvy family member/friend) to come up with the best strategy for you based on your individual goals. The key is to diversify and start early, as you will be surprised how much your savings add up over time.

Finally, you cannot forget that **you still need to have some fun!** You just accomplished your ultimate goal of graduating from veterinary school. You have lived 8'ish years on a strict budget, and like me, you may never be able to look at Ramen again (bye high sodium, no nutritional benefit, yet filling, and delicious entrée). After you have mapped out the main expenses in your budget, you need to ensure there is some left over for the fun stuff. Our job can be stressful and demanding, so you should reward yourself when you deem it necessary. We all have our guilty pleasures, and it is healthy to indulge sometimes. Creating time to decompress is so important when you are in a demanding medical profession. The key is to find a balance, which I am still learning!

7. FIRST DAY
JITTERS

My first day on the floor as an official veterinarian was an unforgettable experience. It felt like a thousand butterflies were fluttering around in my stomach. My first appointment that morning was an 8-week old kitten that was newly adopted from a shelter. I was graced with hour-long appointments initially, for which I am still eternally grateful. I walked into that room confident, or so I thought, and then rambled on for about 40 minutes about everything from vaccines, to normal kitten behavior, to spaying, to hairballs, to household toxins, to different diseases they get, and the list goes on. Thankfully, she was a super-cool girl in her early 20's who just appreciated the knowledge, but goodness did I talk her ear off! I quickly realized that I had to scale back the talking and figure out better time management strategies. You do not have to accomplish everything in one visit. Pay attention to how your clients perceive you, as if you do not make adjustments along the way, it will be a very long first few months.

It is a difficult transition to go from vet school with its three hour long work-ups to 30 minute scheduled appointments or walk-in emergencies. The good news is that most hospitals understand the learning curve and will help you ease into the transition. Don't forget to ask in the job interview process what measures are taken for new graduates so that you know what to expect when you first start out. I found that it was very helpful to have a more experienced assistant, even if just for the first couple of weeks, so they can help you stay on time, teach you how to use the computer software, and help you with your charges. Most hospitals will give you extra catch-up time throughout the day, or start you out with longer appointments for a period of time. These extra steps will give you time to acclimate to the hospital and allow you to feel less stressed as you work through your cases.

There are some helpful things you can do before your first day to make your workdays run a little smoother in the first month. I would start by getting a list from your hospital of all the medications and food products they carry. This will allow you to prepare ahead of time, and you can look up any drugs you may not already know. When you get your first ear infection, it will be a lot less stressful if you already know what options you have to treat that cute Golden Doodle's yeast otitis externa. It also helps when your client inquires about what parasite preventative you recommend for their pet. I ended up making a cheat-sheet in the notes application on my phone with a list of the products I would recommend for various diseases such as my favorite dental chews, joint supplements, shampoos, etc. People love getting advice from us, and this easy preparation will help you with your annual physical exam appointments, so you can confidently provide clients with tips on how to improve the health of their pet.

Smart phones have revolutionized access to information, even within veterinary medicine. Seriously though, what did we do without them?? These gadgets can provide you with immediate access to information that will make your life SO much easier. You will find there are a lot of veterinary applications out there. Technology can help you out tremendously and is a great way to improve your efficiency when nothing seems to come easy in the early days. A personal favorite is the Plumb's drug formulary application, as it allows you to access all your drug dosages instantly. It is much more efficient than the book version, as I have found this is a hot commodity in a teaching hospital. I strongly recommend making a note in your phone with the drugs you find you are using most commonly and their mg/kg (and mg/mL if it is an injection). I can think of at least ten drugs I use almost every day, and this will save you time until you have them memorized: think of your antibiotics, pain medications, common injectables (anti-nausea, gastro-protectants, etc). Other applications you can find include pet food company apps that will navigate you to a good food recommendation, easy calculators for weight loss plans for pets, and the list goes on.

The one area that technology does not help you with is client communication. Unfortunately, we are living in a society that is relying more heavily on emails and texts for quick communication. I find myself texting my friends and family a lot more, and the sad truth is that people are not engaging in face-to-face communication as much as in the past. I know most of you went to veterinary school to work with animals, but let's face it, there is always a human attached to that cute furry patient. Our profession does require human contact, and I am happy veterinary schools are starting to now teach communication and professionalism as a part of the curriculum.

Just as we all have different personalities, you will find that clients are also very different. People are going to respond to news differently, and you have to find ways to adjust your tone and style to each person. Some clients will become extremely emotional, while others may become very quiet. I have had clients screaming and crying during euthanasia, or others who start yelling at me, pointing blame for the loss of their pet. It can be very difficult the first few times you are around an emotional client, and there is not a lot you can do to prepare for it. I have found that the best skill a veterinarian has is to listen and empathize with each client's specific situation. You must find ways to relate to each client and understand that it is normal for people to exhibit extreme emotion for their pets.

It is also important to never pre-judge a client. You always want to offer the gold standard for each patient. You never know what a client is able to afford, so it is best to discuss your plan in detail, and then provide the cost. A tip is that it can be easier to have a support staff member come in with the estimate after you have gone over the plan so that it separates you from the cost. Then, I will be sure to give the client some time to think about what was discussed by leaving the room, and will come back later to discuss things in more detail. This approach gives the client the opportunity to discuss what they can afford, and then allows you to be able to tailor the plan together. Money is always going to be difficult to talk about, and as a veterinarian, our goal is to always offer the best, while working with the specific needs of each family.

There is an art to portraying confidence and being able to effectively communicate with clients. You will quickly learn that it is difficult to have that "first conversation" for each diagnosis or disease. The good news is that repetition will help you build a foundation. You want to be able to discuss your physical exam findings concisely, recommend appropriate diagnostics, and then work through the results followed by the suggested treatment plan. I remember struggling through my first discussion on diarrhea and was cringing thinking back to my rambling conversation about the 20+ reasons a young, 2-year-old dog could develop this symptom. It took me about three to five cases per disease/problem to get my spiel down to where I could confidently guide an owner.

Never forget that first and last impressions are the most important. It seems simple enough, but you need to always have a strong opening when you enter the exam room. You should greet the pet, owner, and then introduce yourself. Please be sure you use the client's name, pet's name, and look up the sex/breed of the pet. I still remember the shame of a client correcting me when I called Fluffy a boy instead of a girl or when I mistook a Norwich Terrier for a Cairn Terrier. It may seem silly, but this is important to an owner and shows them how much you care by taking these little steps. I will then make small talk and segue the conversation into how their pet is doing. This can be informal; I will sit on the floor or a chair directly facing the owner. An aside: please do not have the exam table separating you from the owner, as it can be a barrier and make you seem "closed off." Smile, breathe, and maintain eye contact. You need to be aware of your body language and show you are in control of it. This means no crossed arms, and nice, pleasant facial expressions. From there, have the owner be a part of the exam as much as possible because this tends to make their pet more comfortable and allows you to easily talk about and show the exam findings to them. This will portray to the owner the value of a physical exam and prevents the dreaded awkward silence.

The middle of your client interaction is centered on the diagnostic and treatment plan. You have shown the owner the areas of concern on their pet, and now you need to explain to them what you need to do in order to diagnose and/or treat. My best advice is to keep things simple. You do not want to get into the weeds right away by discussing each differential in detail without a diagnosis. You just want to explain simply what your primary concerns are with their pet, and then discuss the value of the diagnostics in narrowing down your diagnosis. I always try to explain diagnostics as a way of ruling things out. There is nothing more frustrating to an owner than spending $500 and receiving no definitive answers. I quickly learned that if things are worded in the sense of what was ruled out today, then people tend to leave happier. It is ok to sympathize with an owner that the process of diagnosis is frustrating and explain what was determined is not the disease process, along with any tentative diagnoses that may be formulated from the results that day. This way, the value is understood in how you spent their money and allows you to explain the systematic nature of your plan.

I know we are doctors, but truly our profession has become a sales profession. You have to show the value in everything you do! With the rising cost of veterinary care, people need to understand why these tests are important. People are becoming less aware of medical costs because they can leave a human hospital without paying, and then receive a bill months later that is mostly covered by health insurance. Most people do not even look at the entire bill to see the total cost in comparison to what they owe with their deductible. When I broke my leg in vet school, my total bill was around $40,000. With my deductible, I paid about $5,000. That is a HUGE difference! I like to show value by always giving my owners a copy of the lab results so they can hold it in their hands. I will also pull up any x-ray or ultrasound images and talk them through the findings in person. Most owners think this is cool and really enjoy learning about what you have found. Remember to focus the conversation on what you have ruled out instead of saying, "Here is Fluffy's x-ray. It is normal." This can frustrate some owners because they think about what they just spent, and feel like they are in the same position as they were an hour ago with Fluffy.

I do have a quick pet peeve to discuss with you. There is nothing more annoying than when I go for a service or appointment only to be talked over. It can be extremely frustrating when I bring my car to the shop, and the mechanic starts going into a detailed discussion on what is going on with my engine. Do I really know all the bells and whistles that make the engine run? Absolutely not! I just want to know what was found, what needs to be done to fix it, the cost, and when it will be ready. You just had four years of school and have learned an extensive medical vocabulary. These are "million dollar words" that the majority of the world will mispronounce. I know it can be tempting to use these words as you paid big bucks to learn them, but you need to remember people do not know what you are saying to them. It can be as simple as radiograph or e-collar. Most people don't know what these things are, or confuse our "e-collar" for a shock collar. We know this lingo because we use these words every day, so it is important to learn quickly how to divulge information in layman's terms. As a guideline, I will try to use language that a 12-14 year old can understand. If you say a word and your client makes a face, then take note of it and learn from it.

My first scary case when I was solo on my overnight rotation is a great example of this. It was 2 a.m., and I had an icteric, weak dog in front of me. Through my exam and diagnostics, I determined he had I.M.H.A. I was completely overwhelmed and walked into the exam room talking a mile a minute about intravascular vs. extravascular hemolysis, primary vs. secondary causes, and then every single thing I had to do to rule out the potential causes so that I could treat his dog appropriately. I remember the guy looking at me dumb-founded, and saying in a cute southern accent "Ma'am, I have no idea what you just told me." I had to laugh at myself and take a few deep breaths because I noticed I was becoming blue in the face. I went into WAY too much detail and discussed everything at 1,000 words per minute. I basically wasted fifteen minutes diving head-first into the weeds. I learned so much from that interaction though, and it helped me to understand a few important things; I needed to work on finding simple words to describe complex things, talk in a broader sense, and then make sure to "chunk then check" with an owner. It is best to say a few sentences then keep checking in with your owner to ensure they are on the same page. You want to be sure to ask them if what you are saying makes sense or if they have any questions. This system will allow you to control the conversation better.

The ending of your visit will always be what stands out most to an owner. You have to be clear and concise by summarizing what you have found, then describe your plan moving forward. I will always be honest with an owner and let them know that I may not have found the exact diagnosis, but that I do have a plan for today. From there, I explain the next steps if Fluffy isn't getting better and clearly outline when they need to come back. The owner should always leave feeling content that you performed a thorough physical exam, ruled out some potential diagnoses, and that you determined the best plan for their pet in both the short and long-term. Even if the beginning and middle of the visit went well, a poor ending will always leave a client unhappy, as it is the last thing they will remember. Don't forget to close with a formality of some sort to reiterate how it was good to meet them or great to see them again. These little steps mean the world to people in a society where formalities are being replaced by quick abbreviated texts or informal emails.

8. PROFESSIONAL INTERACTIONS

I t certainly goes without saying that we would be nothing without our amazing support staff. Our hospitals just simply would not run, and unfortunately we are finding it is becoming more and more difficult to find trained support staff. It is currently known that veterinary medicine has a higher than average turnover rate when compared to other industries. The overall average turnover rate for our industry is around 29.7%. When you break it down further, veterinary technician turnover rates are around 35%, while the rest of the vet support staff is around 44%. This is pretty high, and will be a source of frustration for you over the years. Recently, it has also been found that veterinary technicians have an average "lifespan" of five years in the field. Turnover is due to a variety of factors that can be beyond our control: salary, benefits, hours, and some leaving for vet school or other professions. There are a few things we can control though, as having doctors who support a positive work environment is an important factor in keeping staff happy and engaged.

My first year out of school was met with green veterinary assistants, which can make for a difficult combination when you are just starting out. I struggled with my efficiency and staying on time for appointments, as I was finding my groove early on. This is a skill that takes time for any doctor to master, but can be improved if you have trained staff to guide you through it. Since there was a higher turnover rate in my hospital compared to the average, I was working with new people all the time and had to play an active role in training. Early on, my personal anxieties and stress caused me to become frustrated and short with staff, and I could see this behavior impacting my workflow. This can be a normal response in a stressful career, especially when you are working on self-confidence. It is important to remember back to when you were a green vet assistant, as we all started somewhere. Despite a challenging, long day, you need to always take into account that you are a role model now, and have a big influence on morale.

As mentioned earlier, I currently work in a teaching hospital with new graduates joining us each year. I have really enjoyed seeing how each doctor brings a different style and practice to their medicine. It can take six or more months to feel confident after graduation, and you will learn a lot about yourself during this time. We all have different strengths and weaknesses, and the sooner you can figure yours out, the better off you will be. The most important attribute for any young doctor is the ability to take constructive feedback willingly and be able to self-reflect. No one is perfect, but in order to be the best doctor, it is necessary to have this skill. We are never going to naturally analyze our own faults or mistakes, so you must utilize fellow staff members and doctors for feedback on your performance in the first year. I have a few starting tips for you, but ultimately it will come down to your ability to grow personally through self-reflection.

I will start with one of my personal mistakes. I learned very early on that my attitude influenced the day. I had a very difficult time managing stress initially, and I remember finding myself reaching my breaking point on busy days where the emergencies piled on. I would notice I was responding to questions with short or direct answers that came across as rude or disengaged. When you are having one of those days, you do not always pick up on it in the moment. I would find I was having a difficult time directing staff, which may have partially been their unwillingness to help me due to my attitude. I was seen as bossy or quick-tempered when really I was just internally struggling with my own lack of confidence and skill as a young doctor. Thankfully, my hospital had semi-annual performance reviews so it was helpful to be given this feedback early on so I could adjust my behavior. Reflecting back, I can see how working on my ability to handle stress has improved my work environment as well as my own job satisfaction. Stress management is still an area of my life I continue to work on in order to benefit both my veterinary career and personal life.

This experience in my first year as a doctor taught me that communication is of the utmost importance. Good communication skills will improve your patient care, job satisfaction, and positively influence your work environment. This skill is mastered through your tone, body language, and attitude. You will notice our field attracts a variety of personalities, and your personality will impact your communication style tremendously. You are setting the tone for the appointment or emergency, so even if you are feeling stressed internally, you need to rely on the confidence that you graduated from vet school. You are the leader and can figure this out. If the staff picks up on your self-doubt, it makes it harder to gain their trust and respect. On the other hand, you also need to be careful in your delivery. Some doctors can come across as rude or condescending when they are seen as barking orders or responding in short direct statements. The staff is looking to us for guidance so you have to walk the line of appearing calm and confident while finding a way to direct your staff in a respectful manner. If you are not happy with a staff interaction, you must realize you are the role model now and need to discuss it with them. It is so much easier to work through these interpersonal issues in the moment or later in the day than to have management get involved. Granted, there are certain instances that need to be handled by management, but if you feel comfortable having the conversation, then it helps to talk about what happened or apologize if you may have hurt someone's feelings. This will make such a difference in promoting a positive work environment and allows you to continue to work comfortably with staff.

There are a few big mistakes I see new doctors make in their first year. The first is freezing under pressure. In this situation, the new doctor comes across as completely overwhelmed and does not provide any direction. This is especially scary when you have a STAT walk in, and the staff wants to know the plan for the patient. Conversely, another big mistake is when doctors jump in and start barking orders at staff. This causes a new doctor to come across as rude or condescending to staff and seem like you are being overly critical. These two situations are completely different, however, the outcome is the same. The staff becomes overwhelmed in both scenarios and loses confidence in the doctor. When this happens, it ultimately affects patient care.

Always remember to treat your staff with respect. Step away when appropriate if you find you need a moment. We have all been there where we just need some time to think or breathe. Personally, I learned to go to the bathroom for a few "deep yoga breaths," and this has allowed me to come back feeling recharged. Find what works for you to help you through these difficult situations. You also should not be afraid to ask for help. There will always be doctors around who can guide you, and it helps for you to learn from them by paying attention to how they handle these cases.

Beyond support staff interactions, you will also experience some differences in your interactions with other veterinarians. As we make up the newer generations, Millennial and Generation Z, we have a reputation that precedes us. Our generation was always pushed by our parents to strive for perfection in many things. This perfectionism was great at getting us into vet school but has been shown to impact us professionally in a lot of ways. The main area I have noticed this in is decision paralysis. When faced with a difficult case, I find new graduates tend to over-think every aspect of the case, and in turn struggle with case organization and making a decision. If a diagnosis is not reached from said diagnostic plan, it becomes a source of stress, as we want to always get an answer for our clients.

As a generation, we really want to perform well and when we feel that we are falling short, it can impact us emotionally. For some, this may come out in compassion fatigue. In others, it may manifest in stressful communication as I touched on above. Doctors in older generations understand that medicine is not going to always find an answer, and struggle with the new generation mindset of constantly trying to be correct and failing to move forward when things aren't perfect. We are seen either as "falling into the weeds" because we cannot seem to focus well to keep moving forward or as "know-it-alls" because we critique everything while always voicing our opinions. This mindset can lead to a new doctor sending a patient for "early" referral if too overwhelmed, whereas an older veterinarian will work the case up thoroughly prior to referral. Previous generations rely less on referral until truly stuck or only tend to consider it if a patient really needs a specialist in that moment. Medicine in prior years relied a lot on "trial and error" where the older veterinarian would see how their patient responded to the treatment plan, and then would do follow-up appointments to assess response to said treatment. A downfall of early referral or sending cases away too prematurely is that it can lead to burnout, as stimulating case management keeps you engaged and fulfilled in your career. I am not saying every Millennial or Generation Z veterinarian will be this way, but it is important to understand that this can become a source of tension as you interact with older veterinary colleagues.

The best advice is to always plan for your interactions with older veterinarians. You will find that they want you to come to them with a thought-out plan. By organizing your thoughts ahead of time, it will be much easier for them to give you advice and not make for a difficult conversation. Your delivery will also influence how they respond to you, as you do not want to ever come across as too meek or too cocky. You need to pay attention to how other colleagues interact with each other and use this as a way to adjust your communication style. You will notice differences in communication between a 60-year-old male veterinarian and a 35-year-old female veterinarian. Older male veterinarians will tend to like cut and dry sentences, data to back up your points, and simplicity. Older female veterinarians will be more willing to empathize with you in your struggles but will want you to still be organized and thought-out in your delivery. It is also important to understand there are multiple ways to approach the same problem. As a new graduate, you could ask three doctors the same question and receive three different answers. It does not mean that two of these answers are wrong, but rather that experience and education provide multiple ways to approach the same problem.

Just remember to be mindful of other veterinarians, especially of different generations, as they are going to have different methods or outlooks on medicine, and communication styles that will differ from you. You need to pay attention to what these veterinarians like if you are to get your voice heard. This generational gap will also translate into how you interact with clients and will be important to keep in mind when in the exam room. By understanding this early on in your career, you will be able to survive by your adaptability to your clinic environment.

No matter how far out you are in your career, you will run into communication differences between other veterinary professionals. The main takeaway is that anyone can have a stressful or bad day, but it is how you choose to recover from it that matters. We are big influencers on morale, and if you understand this early, you will play a large part in improving turnover and staff relations. By learning how to adapt to a variety of personality types, you will navigate through difficult days more effectively. This alleviates a large portion of work stress, which can revolve around inter-personal drama. We need to remember we are all here to treat animals and must find ways to effectively communicate in order to work together as a team. By being self-aware and always improving ourselves, we will become strong team players able to accomplish this goal. Not only will our patients receive excellent care, but we will also have better job satisfaction.

9. SOCIAL MEDIA

I t has blown my mind to witness how social media has taken over in the last two decades. I remember eagerly awaiting my college "vt.edu" email address so I could FINALLY sign up for a Facebook account. In the early 2000's, it used to be required that you could only use Facebook if you were in college. Crazy, right?! Nowadays, it is commonplace for any 15 or 55-year-old to have multiple social media accounts in order to connect, share, and review information. We are just now starting to recognize how much social media is impacting the veterinary profession. It has become an excellent marketing tool to allow veterinary hospitals and professionals to get their name out to the public. It has also served as a way to educate the public with news updates and educational information. Social media has given a voice to the public too, where they can review veterinary hospitals and veterinarians by sharing their experiences with other clients. As you can imagine, social media will play both a positive and negative role in your life as you progress through your career.

There are a lot of positive aspects to social media today that can benefit you as a veterinarian. My favorite is when I get a five-star review from a client. These reviews can turn a bad day around, and it really does help to feel appreciated in a profession where we can be taken for granted sometimes. Positive reviews help market you as a doctor and in turn this can bring clientele to your hospital to see you. I know my hospital has been focusing a lot of attention on maintaining a positive social medial presence, and we have even hired a company to help us with this. The internet has become the number one way clients find a hospital, so if you end up with a large number of positive reviews, this brings your hospital closer to the top of a search engine. Online marketers have found that internet searches for veterinarians have spiked over 150% since last year. Therefore, in a competitive market, your social media presence is incredibly important to focus on. It will also bring you confidence and pride in your job as you get to see how you have impacted the lives of your patients and clients. I would never underestimate the power of a five-star review and consider online reviews as something every practice owner should improve upon in order to stand apart from the competition.

Another area where social media can benefit your business is marketing. I already mentioned positive reviews as one way this can help. The internet provides you with an inexpensive way to reach a large population. I see most hospitals do this through a Facebook and/or Instagram page where events going on at the hospital are posted, special discounts are announced (such as dental month), and photos of pets or doctors can be seen. This humanizes your approach by connecting you to your audience and allows easy marketing through things you are already doing by showing the value of the services your hospital provides for pets. As a new doctor, I do find it helps to be active with these accounts. It can be as simple as taking photos with your patients to be posted online, as this gets your name out there. You can take it a step further and do this through your own personal social media, but you want to keep it professional. If you want to reach an audience through your social media, make sure to either have a separate doctor account or just be careful of what you post or write that is outside of the vet realm. Also, it is a good practice to obtain owner consent. Our society is moving towards an "open book" mentality, and clients really like to get to know their doctors. If this isn't your thing, do not feel pressured to do it. Just know these are simple ways you can utilize to market yourself.

The internet has also become a great way to spread information. I can almost guarantee your client has googled their pet's symptoms before coming to see you. As you know from your own google searches, there is a lot of misinformation out there. I am not going to lie, I have been guilty of falling into the rabbit hole of WebMD'ing my own symptoms. We can really make a difference in ensuring our clients are finding appropriate information through informing them of good resources to use if they mention their online research in the exam room. I make sure they know to find websites that are from veterinary colleges or veterinarians, websites that end with edu, or are from veterinary organizations (AVMA, AAHA, WSAVA, etc). It also helps to have educational handouts you can send home with your clients as a follow-up to your conversation. It may not be your thing, but a lot of veterinary hospitals are posting blogs on common topics as well. This will not only help your clients through education, but will also help with your online presence. As our society continues to rely on the internet, we need to work to control the flow of information. There are already some well-known veterinarians doing this, which is great. It has become an important way to show the value of veterinary care and will hopefully help to get more pets the care they need through education.

As you can imagine, social media can also backfire on us. Unfortunately, those five-star reviews can be followed by a one-star review. You need to be prepared that you will receive a one-star review at some point in your career. You will have to find a way to separate yourself from it mentally. Online reviews are inevitable now, so I recommend using them as a learning opportunity to instead find a way to prevent another one. I still have my first bad review burned into my brain. I do not think I will ever forget it, and it really upset me in the moment. My first bad review was from a client who did not agree with me; their perspective was that I did not treat their pet appropriately. Financially, my hands were tied. I could not run diagnostics, and was only able to treat the symptoms seen by the owner and myself on exam. The sad part was that the pet died at home overnight. It was one of those situations where I did the best I could in the moment. I completely sympathize with the client's concerns and perspective, and ultimately the loss of their pet. What I have taken from these reviews though is that most of the time it is not anything we did necessarily but rather a variety of factors we cannot always control.

Negative reviews can occur for a variety of reasons and certainly can be warranted sometimes. The review world has given a voice to everyone, and I read reviews myself when choosing a restaurant in a new city. It can bring to light issues that should be fixed or improved upon, so I do see them as a necessary evil. Some of the top reasons for a negative review in veterinary medicine revolve around finances and communication. The client can perceive us as the bad guy when they cannot afford to treat their pet. This is a difficult situation for everyone involved, but again is not something you can control. The area you can control is communication. I often see this as one of the more common complaints against newer veterinarians in negative reviews. The art of communication is a skill that takes time to develop. Just remember that if you find you are not vibing well with a client, you may need to change your approach. It helps to stop and ask the client if they have any questions or if there is something they need clarified. By keeping this in the back of your mind, you can work to try to prevent these situations from happening.

Sometimes these reviews can progress to cyber bullying. I have seen clients create a Facebook group or post comments in other forums about a veterinarian, which can end up becoming extremely hurtful. I know veterinarians who have experienced this, and I understand how much anxiety and stress it can cause for them as we start to see it happen more often. I know it is easier said than done, but you have to realize this has nothing to do with you. Some clients will see things differently from you, or have had past bad experiences or personal issues that make them react in this way. Social media is used to make people feel validated, and it is not censored. The problem lies with the client, and you have to find a way to separate yourself from it. All you can really do is understand that this can happen to anyone, so you are prepared for when it does occur. There even is a dedicated team now at the AVMA focused on regulating cyber bullying, and in extreme cases, PLIT and the law can intervene. We are not alone in this, and all we can do is continue to focus on the positive reviews and good case outcomes to keep us motivated in our profession.

When you get a client complaint or bad review, it is important to reach out to the client in some way. Human resources or the business department may do this on a managerial level, so it is good to ask your employer how these situations are handled. When you get a review or complaint that is notable, I would meet with whoever is in charge of these to discuss if further steps are warranted. Most hospitals will have a manager reach out to the client first to get their perspective on the issue. If the complaint has to do with your medicine, it helps to write the client a letter explaining everything that was done and why, so they can have time to review it. Most of the time, this is enough to help provide clients some closure. Typically, clients are writing these complaints in an emotional state and having them go through the process of a letter can give them time for their emotions to cool. Just remember, there are always going to be unhappy people out there, and you are not going to satisfy everyone. In an ideal world, even where things are done perfectly, there will still be someone who finds something to complain about.

10. HOW TO STAY ENGAGED

After you have been out in practice for some time, it is common to feel like your medicine has reached a plateau. You will find you reach a comfortable zone where you may not be pushing yourself as much as you were when you first started out. It is natural and happens to everyone at some point. It took me about three years to feel really confident in my practice, and then I reached my plateau after four years in practice. I started to lose motivation; I was waking up and not wanting to go to work. It felt like it happened overnight and caught me by surprise. I took some time to think about my career up until that point so I could figure out where I wanted to grow as a doctor. As a general practitioner, you will find over time that certain areas will interest you more, and this may change from what you originally liked coming out of school. Over time, you can start to tailor your practice to these interests to maintain your job satisfaction.

I took some time to self-reflect, and decided I wanted to further my skill set, while also finding a way to take an active role in management. The cool thing for us is there are extensive continuing education opportunities out there for us to learn new skills. I decided to focus on dentistry and abdominal ultrasound. I did multiple courses and wet labs, which allowed me to feel more confident in these areas. The key from there is to then use your new skills without fear of failure as you need to perfect them over time in order to gain confidence. I was terrified to do my first abdominal ultrasound, but I had to start somewhere if I was going to get better. A tip on how to "sell" your new skill is to charge less in your training months, and explain that this is due to the fact that you are still learning. Clients appreciate honesty, and I tell them there is a good chance I find an answer for them, avoiding specialty referral. If I do not, then I have more evidence that referral may be the best next step.

With regards to management, I am lucky in that I work for a large hospital with many opportunities. I accepted the role of internship director and have really enjoyed this new path, though I am still learning how to best provide feedback appropriately, motivate, teach, and guide interns through their first year with us. I am so thankful for this opportunity and have really found my passion for mentoring graduating veterinarians. I have a renewed love for my job now that I did not even have when I started out. It is daunting to try to be good at everything, and you will be amazed at how much satisfaction it brings you to focus on the areas you really love.

We spend all this time striving to get into veterinary school and then once we get in, we become focused on graduation. Once out in practice, there is a trend in doctors becoming settled in their career and no longer pushing themselves. We finally reach this ultimate goal, but yet many of us do not feel the need to continue to push ourselves once we get our diploma. There are so many other avenues of growth in our profession outside of continuing

your education by residency/specialization. It is important to think about where you see yourself in 5, 10, and 30
years. This will keep you focused and give you something
to work towards as you progress through your career. It
can be as simple as learning how to perform endoscopy or
as complex as owning a busy, 10 doctor emergency clinic.
If you set goals early, you will be better equipped to reach
them, and will also get more out of your career. Unfortunately, our profession can burn us out if we are not careful,
and the fastest way to do this is to get to the point where
each day feels too routine or monotonous. Some people
really enjoy routine, but if you can see this altering your
feeling toward your career, then you need to start thinking
of ways to stimulate your mind again. We are all go-getters
in veterinary medicine, so we need to remember goal setting does not stop once you get the diploma.

The beginning of your career is especially important for
setting the stage long term. You will want to push yourself outside of your comfort zone early to manage difficult
cases and perform new surgeries. This will allow you to
grow your skill set from the beginning so you can perfect
it over time. By gaining a variety of experiences, you will
improve your marketability and job fulfillment allowing
you better confidence in three to five years. As time pro-
gresses, you will want to decide what areas you really
enjoy and find C.E. opportunities that will teach you these
skills. There is always going to be a place for specialty referral, but we cannot forget that most veterinarians did
these challenging procedures in general practice prior to
specialists becoming mainstream. I am happy to see how
veterinary medicine has progressed to where pets are
valued as family members rather than property, making
clients more willing to get advanced care for their pets. It

is important to learn how to work your patients up to the best of your ability, and if you cannot go any further or become overwhelmed, then it is always best medicine to offer referral if your client can afford it. If the client cannot afford the cost or if there isn't a nearby specialty hospital, you need to push yourself in order to help your patient, especially if it is life or death. You will be amazed at what you can accomplish. We owe it to our patients to provide a range of veterinary care. This will prevent burn out by keeping your mind stimulated through performing complex procedures, diagnostics, and managing difficult internal medicine cases.

Continuing education will become the most important way for you to further your growth over the years. There will be plenty of free opportunities available to you as well as larger conferences you can attend using your C.E. budget. Many of the free options are as easy as attending in-hospital C.E. that is sponsored by drug companies, pet food companies, or outside veterinarians who come in to speak to your clinic. In addition, you will find free sponsored dinners in your city, which will also be a fun opportunity to network with veterinarians in your community. Many local specialists will also provide opportunities to learn from them or come and observe them at work. Outside of local opportunities, you can pretty much find anything you are looking for online. There are conferences all over the world you can attend, and many will also offer wet labs you can pay extra to participate in. These continuing education opportunities will be plentiful over the years and will become the best way for your knowledge to stay current. It is of the utmost importance that we value growth in our career and strive to update ourselves to the newest, most up-to-date practice of medicine if we are to adapt to society's needs.

Practice ownership is another way you can advance your career. By owning a hospital, you will be able to grow your professional skills in regards to leadership, personnel management, marketing, networking, and community outreach. This still remains the best way to gain success in our profession, and in turn, a higher salary. With ownership, there do come added and different stressors that are not present working as an associate. It is important to know and prepare for these so that you can handle them as they come up. The main stress revolves around personnel management, as you have to draw the line between personal and professional relationships, to be respected as the hospital leader. You will have to make the tough calls with regards to things that may not be popular with everyone: scheduling, salary/hourly wage, benefits, time off, policy changes, etc. You have to think about these things from the standpoint of what is best for the business. Other stressors can revolve around the fact that if anything happens to equipment, the building, etc, then you will receive calls or communications even when you are home or on vacation. You are never truly "off" work with practice ownership. Thankfully, you can hire managers and other staff members to lessen the load, and spread the responsibility. The main difference as an owner is that at the end of the day, the success of the hospital is in your hands. You will feel this burden when it comes to making decisions for the hospital in order to keep it a successful business. You will have to make the unpopular calls in order to run the business appropriately. The rewards can well outweigh the stressors, but it can take a certain personality type to be able to separate the personal aspects from the business.

The profession continues to see a notable decline in the number of younger veterinarians going into practice ownership. With less veterinary professionals being willing to own, we are seeing the rise of corporate veterinary practice ownership. Many studies have shown that most young veterinarians already feel saddled with debt upon graduation and do not wish to take on more risk and debt. The important thing to realize about this is that if your practice is successful, this becomes good debt for you because as your practice grows, your value will also increase when you go to sell it to the next owner. There will always be less risk with owning an established, successful clinic vs. starting one from scratch. If you have a spark of interest, I strongly recommend discussing this early with the practice you currently work at to look at options or with local lendors/investors who can help you work out a business plan. Young veterinarians should not be afraid to take the ownership leap as the rewards can be significant, and owning a practice will bring you immense job satisfaction as you create the hospital of your dreams.

If hospital ownership is not for you, it is important to remember that there are still plenty of other options within our field, outside of working directly in a hospital setting. If you find that you are starting to get burnt out on your current path or are having more bad days then good days, it is time to take a step back and think about your options. You may enjoy changing up your routine and trying something new. This could mean a job change to work at a shelter performing spay/neuter procedures every day, working in industry for a pet food or drug company, or even working for a government agency. Other options include telemedicine, house calls, or even relief work at different hospitals. This job change may help to break up the monotony of the routine you have found yourself in and be just the thing you need to feel reinvigorated in this profession.

If a job change is too drastic for you, you may enjoy finding a local club or organization to join that will connect you with your community. I found an opportunity to volunteer at an elementary school career fair to talk about the veterinary profession with third through fifth graders. Not only did the kids love playing with my dog and hearing what I had to say, but it also gave me a renewed sense of love for being a veterinarian. If you like speaking, you can find opportunities locally, or even globally, that allow you to lecture on topics that are important to you. It is also very popular to write blogs and engage in social media as ways to connect with your clientele and fellow veterinarians. This outreach will keep you connected to your community, and you never know when a new relationship may bring an exciting opportunity.

11. WORK-LIFE BALANCE

As we all know, no one goes into the veterinary profession for money. Granted, a few will get rich, but most of us will live comfortably. The main reason we go to vet school is because of our passion to save animals, and better their lives as their advocate. For all the good that we do as veterinarians, there is also a downside. There is an alarming issue that was not talked about five years ago when I was in school, and that is the rising rate of suicide among veterinary professionals. It is staggering to think that our demanding career is causing one in six veterinarians to have suicidal thoughts. The Center for Disease Control released a study recently that examined veterinary mortality rates in the U.S. They found that between 1979-2015 male and female veterinarians were 2-3.5 times more likely to commit suicide compared to the national average. At least 398 veterinarians took their own lives during this time frame. This trend is most concerning because it has been determined that women in our field are even more likely to commit suicide than men. With veterinary medicine becoming more female dominated, this could foreshadow a concerning trend if we are not vigilant. With veterinary suicide on the rise, we are taking a step back and looking at the reasons why.

There are many different reasons why veterinarians may consider taking their own life. Our career saddles us, immediately upon graduation, with staggering debt. Your diploma starts to feel pretty heavy when you realize your loan repayment plan is just around the corner. We all want to start paying off these loans, saving for a big purchase such as a house, spending some money on fun things like travel, and some of us to begin planning for a family. Your mounting debt becomes an immediate stressor, so a lot of us begin working ridiculously long hours to try to make the highest income we possibly can. These long hours bring on burnout quickly, as many are working 50+ hours weekly on average, and a lot of us struggle with our own self-care. Many veterinarians see themselves as caretakers, so we begin to take on added daily stress from our demanding clients. We want to be fixers and we try to please everyone, every single day at work. Compassion fatigue is very real in our profession, and I know I felt it early on in my career. It is not easy to euthanize seven of your ten patients on an emergency shift. It is not easy to try to talk to an owner about quality of life when they want you to save their extremely ill and dying 17-year-old cat and have unrealistic expectations for the future. It is not easy to euthanize a pet due to finances. These situations weigh on us emotionally, physically, and mentally. Unfortunately for us, this can be just another typical day at work.

With mounting debt, long hours, difficult clients, and compassion fatigue, we are dealt a tricky hand compared to other professions. We have significant pressure placed on us on a daily basis. I know there are plenty of workdays where I can barely drink a glass of water, go to the bathroom, or take an actual lunch break. I rarely have the luxury of an hour lunch break, and I am five years out of school. My "lunch hour" is spent scarfing down my food in three minutes, and then finishing medical records or calling clients where each phone call is a minimum of five to ten minutes due to clients not realizing how busy I am. My goal of working through lunch is to "hopefully" leave work on time that evening. I know many veterinarians feel this way so this is becoming a big issue.

I feel there are three areas we can adjust to try to help ourselves with these significant work demands. For one, set boundaries! Please for the love of the job, do not leave work and continue to "live work." Stop checking emails from work or clients while at home. Stop talking about that difficult case you had and what you could have done better. We must take time to unwind and focus on something outside of our job. The second thing you can do is to transition your boundaries into self-care. They go hand in hand, as we must take care of ourselves. Outlets outside of work help us to recharge our batteries and feel better about going to work the next day. Try to seek out a job where your employer also values and supports self-care. I know there are still employer mentalities out there of "Well, I worked that hard when I was your age so you need to also." Some jobs may also make you feel like you have to be a production machine, which will lead to a feeling of being overworked. The good news is that we can have some control over these specific areas in the job search.

It is easier said than done to set boundaries. Some vets are better at it than others. I will tell you one of my mistakes, and hopefully, it will help you. I fell down the slippery slope of giving a few clients my email address. Early on, I felt this would create a bond with them as their primary doctor. The complicated part is that some clients will take advantage of you, and there have been some days where I receive multiple emails from the same client. Most of the time, responsible clients will just email regarding follow up on a previous visit. There are other clients who will try to seek out medical advice routinely and utilize your personal email address as a way to avoid a veterinary visit. I have since set better boundaries where I will respond within three to five days instead of within a few hours of reading the email as I did previously. I will not respond to these emails when I am off work and will still tell owners they need to come in if they are just seeking advice.

Smartphones are helpful in many ways but difficult in others because phones keep us constantly connected. You may find that you are using your cell phone to text a family member and then here comes an alert from your work email. My hospital uses Slack for in-hospital communication, which is great in that we can easily disseminate information. However, there may be days where I receive six to eight slack communications in a row. In order to decompress from work, I have set it up where I do not receive instant alerts from slack or my work email when I am off or on vacation. I will even turn my phone off sometimes. If something is extremely important, I will either receive a call or the person will find an answer through someone else. We owe it to ourselves to not "live-work" because it is a fast track to burn out.

Outside of setting boundaries, I truly believe you cannot take care of others if you do not take care of yourself. Self-care is of the utmost importance, especially for those in the medical profession. What is self-care? It can represent different things to different people, and the dictionary definition is "care of the self without medical or other professional consultation." We each should figure out what it means for us. It can be as simple as dedicating one hour out of your day to something you like to do. For some, it is sitting in bed watching Netflix. For others, it may be a creative outlet such as painting. Blowing off steam is healthy, and it is important to figure out the best outlet for you.

It took me a while to figure out what recharged my batteries. I had to find a balance between my healthy and unhealthy favorite pastimes. Wine is great, but in excess, it will end up doing the opposite of what we want it to do. I figured out that working out is what helps me to unwind. I have started going to work out classes because I love the camaraderie of being in a room with others. It pushes me beyond what I would do on my own, and I cannot cancel a class without a fee once I sign up so it keeps me accountable. At the closing of one of my favorite barre studio classes, the instructor will always say this phrase, and it has really stuck with me. "Thank you for carving out an hour of your busy day just for yourself. By taking care of yourself, it allows you to take better care of your loved ones." I know it is a little cheesy, but it is true! I can see a positive change in my body, and in turn, it has made me feel better on a daily basis. This one-hour spent in the studio is the only time in my entire day where I actually shut off my brain.

Despite our best efforts, we will still have bad days that we have to overcome. Our work life is never going to be perfect, so we must constantly work to find new ways to cope. I know some of my bad days can still end with me coming home from work bursting into tears and then drinking a few glasses of wine while I vent to my husband. The important thing to recognize is that we CAN show emotion. It is ok if you have had a rough day. You need to vent about it! We all need a support system, and you can do this by talking on the phone to someone close to you or discussing it with your friend or partner. By holding these emotions in, they start to eat away at us. We all have bad days, and some people are just better at hiding this fact than others. I know that when I acknowledge a bad experience and work through it at an appropriate time, I instantly feel better. I know no one wants to hear "cry it out," but in whatever form this means to you, do it! Do not be afraid to be vulnerable, we all need support, and bad days should not be spent alone.

When you find you are having more bad days than good days at work and are starting to see the glass as half empty, it is time to take a step back. In a profession with a rising rate of suicide and depression, we have an obligation to look out for each other as best we can and support one another. It is important to find a way not to fear help but to ask for it when needed. If you are experiencing depressive thoughts or finding areas of your life that are becoming more difficult, help is out there. I know we can be afraid to ask for help due to vulnerability, but there are many ways you can do so discretely. I have seen many online support groups out there, specifically 'Not One More Vet/ NOMV' stands out to me currently. It is an outlet where veterinarians can compare experiences, and it functions as a wonderfully supportive community. The AVMA is also working on a nationwide mental health education initiative. I know many employers have free assistance programs you can utilize where you start by anonymously talking to someone on the phone. Your employer will have no idea who utilizes the service due to confidentiality, and it allows you to work with a professional to see if further assistance may be helpful in your specific situation. It is never too late to seek professional help, and mental health professionals are great at acting as an outside perspective for us.

Our profession will always have aspects to it that are emotionally, mentally, and physically draining. There is just no way anyone can adequately plan for it, but we can prepare. My hope is that awareness and continuing to talk about this very real issue will help us look out for each other in our profession. By standing together, we can work to overcome rising suicide statistics. If we prioritize taking care of ourselves, then we will be better doctors for our patients.

12. EPILOGUE

I can guarantee either a colleague or you have stated at some point to a hopeful undergrad "Don't go to vet school. If I could do it over, I would go to medical school instead..." It is almost a funny joke now around our hospital as many of our veterinarians have said this to an optimistic veterinary assistant applying to vet school. I have been guilty of this myself saying I would rather be a human dentist instead. And I mean, am I really serious?! I love teeth, but let's be honest here...I would definitely take a dachshund with stage IV/IV dental disease over a human mouth ANY day. Most hopeful veterinary students do not always process, or they push aside, the tough aspects of the job. Don't get me wrong; there will be incredible days where you feel like you are on top of the world saving patients left and right. There will also be difficult days when you have zero motivation to go to work after you just spent fifteen hours there the day before. How is it that we continue to successfully ride this roller coaster of veterinary medicine?

I truly believe our profession requires a special kind of person. I do not know many professions or professionals who can quickly transition from an anal gland abscess appointment to a first kitten visit to a blocked cat emergency to an aggressive dog that wants to tear your face apart during a routine check-up. You will have days where you walk into work on a Monday morning and immediately get seven phone calls from your high maintenance client citing their ridiculous demands. You will have to euthanize a dog that you watched grow up from puppyhood where the owners feel like family after thirteen years together. You will encounter a horrible incident where a pet dies unexpectedly under anesthesia during a routine procedure. You will experience stress colitis when you have to write and mail that international health certificate for Princess Powerpuff with seventy-two hours left before their departure to Italy. There will be ridiculously long days where you took care of 25+ patients, and then have to stay three hours late to write medical records. These events will happen often, and it only takes one to sour an entire work week.

No matter what situation is thrown at you, there will always be hurdles you have to jump over daily. When these bad days happen, sometimes all you can do is laugh it off or drink a glass of wine (or three). We have chosen to work in a profession that deals with life and death on a daily basis, and it is not for everyone. We need to remember that we are not alone and must work together to find ways to cope with these common stressors. When you have been out 5-10+ years and start to feel jaded, it will help to reminisce on the good ole' days when veterinary medicine was just a dream. Do not get me wrong, it is easy to get burnt out by needy clients, production demands, and saying goodbye to your favorite patients. By remembering how it felt to get into veterinary school, I can almost guarantee it will help put things back into perspective for you.

One of the top five moments of my life was when I received my acceptance letter to vet school. I did not get in when I applied my first time around so I spent my year off after undergrad working at a busy small animal general practice. The exact details are hazy, but I remember working that day on appointments with a veterinarian. I knew acceptance emails would be sent out any moment and found myself routinely refreshing my Gmail account. Suddenly, an email from Virginia Tech popped up with the status "You have been offered a position with the Class of 2014!" I am pretty sure I emitted a high-pitched scream and started jumping up and down ecstatically while scaring every dog and cat in the building at that moment. After working so hard, it was the craziest feeling to finally know I was on the road to my dream job. What got me thinking about this moment was being lucky enough to recently experience a staff member get into vet school. She also received an email like me while at work, and I could literally feel the happiness bubbling off of her. It was so refreshing to witness! Moments like these help to reinvigorate us again and remind us to remember how much this profession really means to us.

Veterinary medicine will always be a field that is adapting and changing to the needs of our patients and the expectations of our clients. We are part of a dynamic profession that is forever evolving, and we must accept these changes in order to maintain our job satisfaction. My hope for you is that this book brought to light some of the hot topics in our field as well as some of the important differences seen today as a practicing Millennial or Gen Z veterinarian. I have provided you with guidelines to cultivate your own success while giving you the tools to feel adequately prepared in your professional life. I would not be where I am today without the mentorship I have been given and the strong bond I feel to my hospital and fellow staff members. It is up to us, as veterinarians, to work together as a

Ashley Gray

profession to help each other throughout our careers. We cannot function as independents, and I believe that if our profession fosters a strong support system, then together we can work through all of the challenges we face in society today. By taking care of one another, we will be able to take better care of our patients. I challenge you to always remain an advocate for not only your patients but for your colleagues and yourself as the years go by.

RESOURCES:

<u>Helpful "Pocket" Books for Clinics and Graduation</u>
- The Small Animal Veterinary Nerdbook by Sophia Yin
- Small Animal Medical Differential Diagnosis by Mark S. Thompson
- Emergency Procedures for the Small Animal Veterinarian by Signe J. Plunkett
- Guide to Small Animal Clinics by Susan and Chris Pasquini, and others

<u>Helpful Apps for your Phone</u>
- Plumb's Veterinary Drugs
- Merck Vet Manual: explanations on thousands of health conditions
- Vet-Anatomy: atlas of animal anatomy
- Each pet food company has an app so you can load your favorites (usually in the form of product guides, weight loss apps, diagnostic apps to determine best prescription diet, etc)
- Dog Scanner and Cat Scanner: my favorite for bonding with clients…not completely accurate but gives you an idea of what breeds are present within a pet

<u>Job Posting Websites</u>
- AVMA: https://jobs.avma.org/jobseekers
- iHire Veterinary: https://www.ihireveterinary.com
- Indeed: http://www.indeed.com
- Glass Door: http://www.glassdoor.com
- Linked In: http://www.linkedin.com

<u>Licensing:</u>
- AVMA website has a list of each State Medical Board Website to make it easy to compare requirements state to state
  - https://www.avma.org/KB/Resources

- AVMA Membership Information
  - https://www.avma.org/Members/HowToJoin/Pages/default.aspx
- AVMA Professional Liability Insurance
  - http://www.avmaplit.com
- DEA Licensing
  - https://apps.deadiversion.usdoj.gov

Wellness:

- Headspace: meditation website with an app
- Mindbodygreen: website covering a variety of topics from healthy recipes, fitness advice, mental health, relationship talk, etc
  - http://www.mindbodygreen.com
- Talkspace: online therapy with a licensed therapist
- Suicide Prevention Hotline: 1-800-273-8255

About the Author:

Dr. Ashley Gray was born and raised in Virginia and received her veterinary degree from Virginia-Maryland Regional College of Veterinary Medicine. Upon graduation, she completed a one-year rotating small animal internship at a busy general practice with 24-hour emergency care. After her internship, she decided to stay on as a general practitioner and emergency doctor. She is still hard at work at this practice and has recently taken on the role of Internship Director. She lives in Charlotte, North Carolina with her husband, 2 dogs, and 2 cats. In her downtime, you will find her cuddling her cats with Netflix, trying out new restaurants, and traveling.

She has always had a passion for writing, even at a young age. There are many unpublished "Clifford the Big Red Dog" novels to prove it lying around her mother's home. She is extremely passionate about the veterinary profession, especially as it relates to mentorship and self-care. This is her first novel; her intention is to be part of a support system that helps each graduating class succeed in Veterinary Medicine. Through her firsthand experience, "Becoming a Millennial Veterinarian" is going to bridge the gap for many young doctors navigating the waters as they transition from student to professional.

MILLENNIAL
VETERINARIAN

Made in the USA
Middletown, DE
05 December 2021

54295347R00061